Bulimia, Binge-eating and their Treatment

PROFESSOR J. HUBERT LACEY,
DR BRYONY BAMFORD
and
AMY BROWN

sheldon PRESS

We would like to thank our patients who have taught us everything. They and their families have allowed us to enquire into often painful issues and periods of their lives that they might otherwise have wished to forget. From this generous information the treatment described here has been developed.

First published in Great Britain in 2010

Sheldon Press
36 Causton Street
London SW1P 4ST
www.sheldonpress.co.uk

British Library Cataloguing-in-Publication Data
A catalogue record for this book is available from the British Library

ISBN 978–1–84709–035–5

1 3 5 7 9 10 8 6 4 2

Typeset by Fakenham Photosetting Ltd, Fakenham, Norfolk
Printed in Great Britain by Ashford Colour Press

Produced on paper from sustainable forests

Contents

Note to the reader

This is not a medical book and is not intended to replace advice from your doctor. Consult your pharmacist or doctor if you believe you have any of the symptoms described, and if you think you might need medical help.

Preface and acknowledgements

Preface

Just over 30 years ago, a 'new' illness was described in the UK. It was debilitating and it severely affected the lives of young people, particularly women. It was called bulimia nervosa, and soon descriptions of it were reported in the medical and lay press throughout North America and Europe.

Bulimia nervosa sufferers have low self-esteem and feel that control, especially over food, has been removed from them. They are depressed and often angry. Their relationships with both men and women are affected. There are physical complications too, some of which are dangerous. Yet bulimia often remains, to the individual, a secret disorder. Most people who binge-eat do not tell friends or family; they are alone with their disorder. This book, then, is for them: to give them knowledge and to instil hope. Through this book, people with bulimia can understand more about their feelings and behaviours and how they can effect change. In essence, the book shows how they can help themselves.

The approach described in this book is effective, but if you are unable to benefit, you must seek other help. Your GP should always be approached first because she or he will know of local treatment centres. Never forget that bulimia and binge-eating are treatable.

I am grateful for the significant contribution to this book made by Dr Bamford and Ms Brown, who undertook the majority of the writing.

Professor J. Hubert Lacey, London

Acknowledgements

The authors would like to thank Amelia Bamford, Rebecca Ramsden, Charlotte Evans and Francesca Sawer for their valued contributions to this book.

About the authors

Prof J. Hubert Lacey is Emeritus Professor of Psychiatry at the University of London. He is Clinical Director of the Eating Disorders Unit at the Capio Nightingale Hospital in central London, treating adults and adolescents. He is Medical Director of the Newbridge Hospital, Birmingham, treating children and adolescents with eating disorders. He developed the St George's Eating Disorders Service in London into the largest NHS service. He has also been Director of the Yorkshire Centre for Eating Disorders in Leeds and the Peninsula Eating Disorders Service in Exeter. He is a graduate of the Universities of St Andrews, Dundee and London and is a Fellow of the Royal College of Psychiatrists. He is Chairman of the European Council on Eating Disorders and is Patron of Beat, the user and carer charity for the UK. Professor Lacey has published over 140 publications on anorexia nervosa, bulimia nervosa and obesity. He defined a new syndrome of multi-impulsive bulimia, has developed new treatments for eating disorders and has won the NHS Modernisation Award.

Dr Bryony Bamford is a specialist clinical psychologist with the St George's National Eating Disorders Service, South West London and St George's Mental Health NHS Trust, and an honorary Research Fellow at St George's, University of London.

Amy Brown is currently studying at Royal Holloway, University of London, towards a doctorate in clinical psychology. Previously she worked at St George's, University of London, as a research assistant for the eating disorders team and as an honorary assistant psychologist for the National Eating Disorders Service, South West London and St George's Mental Health NHS Trust.

Part 1
BULIMIA AND BINGE-EATING

1

Introducing bulimia and binge-eating

Eating disorders are increasingly talked-about but still relatively misunderstood disorders. And, even though anorexia nervosa and bulimia nervosa are now quite well known, they are surprisingly less prevalent than a relatively unknown eating disorder known by the acronym EDNOS, or eating disorder not otherwise specified.

These three, in addition to a fourth, binge-eating disorder, which is binge-eating in obesity, are all allied conditions. However, the relationships between them and the diagnostic differences are, to some extent, still unclear. The aim of this book is to bring some clarity to these related disorders, to educate the reader about the factors that cause and maintain binge-eating, a behavioural aspect of each of the named disorders, and to take the reader through a specialized 'treatment programme' designed to help individuals who binge-eat but want to stop.

What is binge-eating?

Binge-eating is eating a large amount of food in a brief period of time. Attempting to define 'large' and 'brief' leads everyone into a mess! They are best left undefined; after all, most people binge, particularly at certain times of year such as Christmas or holidays. In these instances, however, it certainly does not represent an illness. Really it is the frequency and persistence, coupled with distress, that stamps binge-eating as an illness. Eating must be paired with an extreme loss of control for it to be accurately termed a 'binge' – this is what differentiates it from simply overeating. Put simply, you will know when it represents an illness. Equally distressing is when binge-eating is associated with other behaviours such as self-induced vomiting, or taking laxatives as a means of compensating for the food eaten during binge-eating. This book will also deal with many of these associated behaviours.

What happens during a binge?

Binge-eating, when it is an illness, is a solitary pursuit. The person frequently buys special binge foods. These are easy to eat, requiring little preparation or cooking, and are usually, although not always, high in fats and sugars. Very large amounts of food can be eaten. We have known people eat up to 30,000 kilocalories a day, nearly 15 times the calories needed to maintain normal metabolism. More usually, however, a person will eat two or three times his or her normal dietary intake and often only on certain days of the week.

Bingeing is usually done in private, if not in secrecy. It is, to the person with the condition, the most humiliating behaviour. Frequently no one else will know about it, or if it is suspected it will be vigorously denied. In addition, food is rarely eaten in a socially acceptable way during a binge and occasionally rather bizarre behaviours take place, such as spitting out some of the food, eating extremely quickly or smearing food over the body or elsewhere.

Bingeing usually starts off as an exercise that is enjoyable, guilt-free and often exciting or thrilling. The person may look forward to and plan for his or her binges. Sadly, however, it rarely stays this way. Following a binge, people may view their actions as disgusting, humiliating and degrading. Guilt-ridden, they may engage in further behaviours, such as vomiting or using laxatives in an attempt to neutralize these distressing emotions. These actions, often termed 'compensatory behaviours', are undertaken in an attempt to get rid of the excess and feared calories consumed during the binge. However, it is these behaviours that lead to the even more intense shame, distress and humiliation described by those who binge and purge. It is devastating behaviour which can have a profound effect on the person's ability to conduct his or her working and social life. At its very worst, it becomes all-preoccupying, both a loved and intensely feared behaviour.

Binges are often divided into 'objective binges' and 'subjective binges'. 'Objective binges' refers to the definition of a binge given above, i.e. eating an unusually large amount of food for the situation you are in, such as a whole family pack of crisps, a whole loaf of bread or a whole pack of biscuits. A 'subjective binge' refers to eating a small or normal amount of food, usually more than you want to eat but not unusual for the circumstances. Both, however, are accompanied by a sense of loss of control, which is what characterizes them as binges.

Diagnosis

The diagnosis of bulimic disorders, whether they occur at normal weight (as in bulimia nervosa), in obesity (as in binge-eating disorder) or at low weight (as in the bulimic form of anorexia nervosa), is confused and contentious. We will try and bring some light to the matter. The treatment section of this book is aimed at those who binge at a normal weight. While we do not consider the treatment programme here to be suitable for those at a low weight, we will none the less describe anorexia nervosa here in order to put the different eating disorder diagnoses into context for the reader.

Anorexia nervosa

Anorexia nervosa is the least common but most severe eating disorder. To be diagnosed with anorexia you have to be at a very low weight (below a body mass index, or BMI, of 17.5; for more on BMI, see pages 86–7). It has a high morbidity, meaning it gives rise to much physical illness. It also has the highest mortality of any disorder in psychiatry and is even more dangerous than alcoholism or drug addiction. It is estimated that between ten and 20 per cent of people with the condition die prematurely, either by suicide or starvation. Anorexia has occurred throughout history, but it only received its name in 1873. Unfortunately it is a rather bad name! Anorexia means lack of appetite, which is particularly inappropriate as most anorectics are ravenous. It occurs in approximately 0.7 per cent of girls and women aged between 16 and 40 years.

Anorexia is essentially a phobia of being a 'normal weight', meaning that the person drives herself to gross emaciation. It is rare for someone with anorexia to ever reach a weight that she is able to feel happy with, however emaciated she becomes. Even at life-threateningly low weight, people with anorexia will still feel themselves to be and describe themselves as 'fat'. The weight loss in anorexia can be due to dietary restriction, overactivity or self-induced vomiting. It may also follow laxative or diuretic abuse. This weight loss, which commonly starts off as dieting, results in someone who is physically, emotionally and socially impaired, far different from how she was before the disorder took hold.

Anorexia usually occurs in adolescence. It usually begins shortly after puberty. By early adulthood, if untreated, it can become chronic and enduring, and increasing difficult to treat. Treatment for anorexia at any stage is difficult, and for some people the condition will be life-long.

Anorexia, like all the eating disorders, is much more common in women and girls than men or boys. This is probably for biological as well as emotional and social reasons. We look at this later (see pages 10–11). It is sometimes claimed that about ten per cent of anorectic sufferers are male. This is almost certainly an overestimation as the data comes from research centres where it's more likely that an 'unusual' boy would be treated than a 'routine' girl. It is probably the case, however, that the prevalence of anorexia in men is increasing as a reflection of an increased preoccupation with appearance by men or emphasis on sporting achievement.

It used to be that almost all people with anorexia nervosa restricted or 'dieted' to lose weight. Now the majority purge, with or without binge-eating. Indeed, since anorexia in its pure form is so difficult to maintain, the vast majority of people will end up binge-eating, with purging being a resulting, compensatory, strategy. It is in this instance that the illness can be commonly confused with bulimia nervosa.

This book, however, is not directed towards those who have a 'binge–purge' form of anorexia, i.e. those who are bingeing at a low weight. This book is rather aimed at those who experience binge-eating at a normal or higher weight. Binge-eating in this context is discussed next.

Bulimia nervosa

Bulimia nervosa occurs at normal body weight. The person may be very unhappy with his or her body and want to lose weight, but this tends to be less intense than the driven emaciation of anorexia. Although weight is within a normal range, it does fluctuate in response to the assaults of binge-eating. This fluctuation can be quite marked, often between 5 and 8 kg.

Unlike anorexia nervosa, bulimia normally starts in early adulthood or late adolescence. The average age of onset of binge-eating is 17 to 18 years and on average self-induced vomiting begins about three years after the binge-eating. Most people with bulimia wait up to five years before seeking help. This pattern is quite different from anorexia, where the illness is clear from an early age. Sometimes, however, the picture is confused because normal-weight people with bulimia may have experienced a brief episode of weight loss in mid-teenage years. This is referred to as 'cryptic anorexia'. It rarely lasts more than a few months, but seems to prepare the scene for the future presentation of bulimia nervosa itself.

In their extreme forms, the psychological feelings that exist in bulimia nervosa are quite different from those in anorexia. In bulimia there is not always a driving or preoccupying fear of normal weight. Undoubtedly the person would like to weigh less, but the thought of being emaciated, with skeletal appearance, is usually as undesirable to the bulimic as it is to a normal person. Clearly, though, people with bulimia are not without distressed feelings. Individuals with bulimia will place a huge amount of importance on their weight and shape, and generally will experience an overwhelming desire to be slimmer or to rigidly control their weight. A common concern is the sense of being out of control and the fear of losing control of their weight. Because of the extreme importance that is placed by the person on shape and weight, contemplating losing control over his or her weight is a terrifying experience. Usually this fear of losing control, paired with occasional loss of control, is restricted to eating and food. Sometimes, however, it may extend to other aspects of the person's life. For example, sometimes he or she may feel out of control when drinking alcohol or using other social drugs. It can also lead to overspending or to unwanted sexual experiences. This is known as multi-impulsive bulimia and is a severe variant.

EDNOS

EDNOS, or eating disorder not otherwise specified, is a 'rag-bag diagnosis', and it's estimated that up to ten per cent of adult women are affected. The term is used when a person does not have all the features of anorexia or bulimia – for instance, someone with anorexia who menstruates regularly, or someone who repeatedly vomits at normal weight but does not binge-eat. Owing to the complexities of diagnosis, around three-quarters of individuals with diagnosed eating disorders will fall into this category.

Binge-eating disorder

Binge-eating disorder is the presence of binge-eating without the resultant compensatory behaviours (i.e. vomiting, laxative abuse, extreme dieting or exercise). This tends to be seen in more overweight or obese people but is different from merely being overweight. The binge-eating again involves the consumption of excessive amounts of food in a short period of time during which the individual experiences a sense of loss of control, to the extent that he or she would not be able to stop eating if interrupted by the phone or doorbell. This is as much an eating disorder as anorexia or bulimia nervosa, but is less commonly recognized.

The differences between anorexia and bulimia

Although both bulimia and anorexia may include recurrent binge-eating, there are differences. Apart from the obvious ones of anorexia being at low weight while bulimia is at a normal or higher weight, in anorexia there is in addition an intense fear of normal weight; in bulimia, although the person's self-evaluation is unduly influenced by weight and shape, which may cause significant distress, fear of weight tends to lack a phobic intensity. In both, the person may be sad or depressed. However, in bulimia, the person tends to be impulsive and to swing between being overcontrolled and abandoning control, whereas in anorexia the person tends to be rigid, often perfectionist and withdrawn. In both, the eating disorder can lead to significant social difficulties. Research also suggests that whereas the anorectic develops her illness in early adolescence, individuals tend to develop bulimic behaviours somewhat later. These behaviours may vary during an individual's illness. If, however, they have the core feelings of anorexia – a phobia of normal weight – these will remain, irrespective of weight.

Because of the obvious low weight in anorexia, people often recognize that the individual has an eating disorder, whereas bulimia can be hidden much more easily. Some people – even those suffering from bulimia themselves – believe that you can't have an eating disorder if you are at a normal weight, but this is *not* true.

Physical consequences

Binge-eating and vomiting can give rise to a number of physical problems. Indeed, the physical risks associated with binge-eating and the impact on the body can be very serious and should not be underestimated. The majority of the risks associated with bulimia are non-visible, for example the impact on the heart, gastrointestinal system, fertility, brain and kidneys. Some of the consequences, however, are visible. Perhaps the most distressing can be the swelling of the salivary glands in the neck, which some people describe as making them look rather like a hamster. In addition, repeated vomiting can cause a rebound water retention which may cause the legs and thighs to 'swell'. Many people feel that they look bloated, or even fat, as a result of these physical changes. Repeated vomiting is likely to lead to erosion of the teeth, with discoloration and loss of fillings being a common, distressing and expensive consequence of this behaviour. Finally, bingeing can also have an impact on mood, concentration and social life, which can understandably be very distressing for the person and contribute to a reduced quality of life. All of these consequences will be discussed in more detail later in the book.

What causes binge-eating?

There are as many causes of eating disorders as there are people with disordered eating. For each individual, the origin of an eating disorder is a unique blend of underlying and precipitating factors which prompt the urgent need to abuse food. Many of these factors are discussed in detail in the following chapters. The point to make here is that there are many risk factors, which in any one person provide only a partial explanation. For a small minority there is adverse parenting, and sexual abuse may be implicated in an even smaller number. Much more common is the impact of being brought up in a family where there is much interest in dieting, fashion and shape. Often mentioned by people are critical comments during their teenage years about their shape and weight, while others claim societal pressure to be slim. Other eating disorders in the family, depression or misuse of drugs or alcohol can all provide the background in which binge-eating and bulimia may flourish. All eating disorders are generally linked to a low self-esteem and low mood. Really, though, there is not one factor which marks out the future binge-eater.

Who develops binge-eating?

Certainly anyone can develop binge-eating. It is not restricted to gender, class or culture. It is the case, though, that these disorders tend to be seen more prevalently in women, tend to start in adolescence or early adulthood, and tend to affect those living in Western or modern societies to a greater extent. This is not to say that people outside these categories do not develop binge-eating disorders but, rather, there exists a greater vulnerability or pressure in young Western females. We will discuss why this might be next.

Throughout history, the fashionable body weight has changed significantly. The hourglass figures depicted in paintings from the seventeenth century and displayed by Hollywood actresses until the 1950s are quite different from the ultra-slender and often emaciated figures displayed in the media today. Females, indeed, are 'fattier' than males and this is seen across a number of different species, not just the human form. In humans, however, 'shape' forms the basis of sexual attraction, a difference from any other species, where attraction is more commonly based on smell or colour. The underlying issues of weight and shape are therefore rooted in core aspects of femininity and human sexuality.

Interestingly, there is no evidence to support the notion that any particular body shape or size is more appealing to men than any other. Furthermore, there is no evidence that men are drawn to women who are very slim. Indeed, there is no evidence that men are drawn to any particular shape or weight in their partners. There is, however, evidence that it is women who prefer women to be slim.

The exact influence of the media in disorders of weight and shape is still debated; however, it is clear that there exists a strong message that women should be appealing on the outside to be valued by others, i.e. that the way they look is central to happiness and success.

In adolescence there exists a vulnerability to confusion, low self-esteem and emotional insecurity. This is a vulnerability that perhaps does not exist in less developed countries where, when young girls become wives or mothers much earlier, there is little gap between childhood and adulthood. It would be unsurprising that those who are unsure and vulnerable develop behaviours which give transient support in the face of an uncertain world. Binge-eating in women can perhaps be mirrored by alcohol misuse in men.

In Western societies, where the role of women has changed dramatically with economic advancement, social and cultural pressures on women have contributed to a backdrop of unsure-ness and low self-esteem in some. More vulnerable women, seeking to enhance their self-esteem and aware that initial social attractiveness is based on appearance, may try to control or restrict their figures to stay 'youthful' or 'more attractive'. This restriction in eating, however, done in order to reduce weight, is the very thing that causes binge-eating, a link that will be explored further in subsequent chapters.

Summary

- A binge is defined as eating a large amount of food combined with an extreme sense of loss of control.
- Bulimia is the presence of binge-eating paired with any number of compensatory behaviours (vomiting, laxative use, excessive exercise and dieting, diuretics) used as a way of influencing shape and weight. People with bulimia tend to base their self-esteem and self-worth on their satisfaction with their shape and weight.
- Bulimia occurs at a normal weight or higher; at lower weights, bingeing occurs within an anorectic pathology.
- While bingeing tends to be more common in Western female adolescents, anyone can develop bingeing disorders for any number of reasons.
- Bingeing in any form is a distressing, guilt-ridden and shameful experience which affected people generally feel unable to tolerate or to stop.

2

Causes and consequences

Risk factors

As discussed in the previous chapter, there are many reasons why people develop a problem with binge-eating. The origin of an eating disorder is complex and unique to each individual, but we are aware of a number of factors which increase the chance of developing a problem with binge-eating, and we term these 'risk factors'. Risk factors include all experiences that put people at risk of abusing food. People often mention, for example:

- having been criticized in the past about their body or eating habits;
- having a problematic or invalidating relationship with their parents or significant others early in their lives;
- involvement in certain sports or leisure activities (such as gymnastics or ballet) which place demands on young women to be a certain weight or size.

In addition to these risk factors, other factors can also play a part in someone developing an unhealthy relationship with food: for example,

- a family history of eating disorders
- depression
- substance misuse
- obesity
- chronic dieting.

Individual characteristics too can be possible risk factors for developing an eating disorder, including:

- low self-esteem
- perfectionism

- anxiety problems
- previous obesity.

Maintaining factors

Once a problem with bingeing has begun, an individual may feel caught in a destructive pattern he or she will never be able to break. There are a number of factors which can keep this vicious cycle going, and we call these 'maintaining factors'.

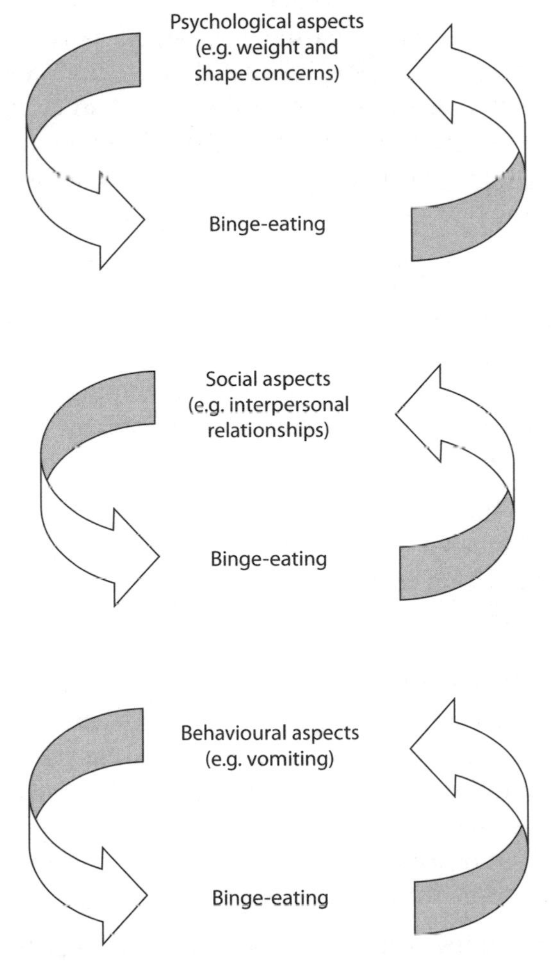

Figure 1 Maintaining factors in binge-eating

Broadly speaking, maintaining factors can fit into three dimensions:

1 psychological aspects
2 behavioural aspects
3 social aspects.

Psychological and behavioural aspects are covered in this chapter, social aspects in Chapter 3. These dimensions are interwoven, but separating them out helps to create clarity when trying to understand this complex problem.

The different aspects discussed next are so powerful in maintaining the disordered eating because they are both a cause *and* a consequence of binge-eating. This means a vicious cycle is created, whereby the very reasons for bingeing are made more prominent by the bingeing itself, continuing the cycle of binge-eating (see Figure 1 on the previous page).

Psychological aspects

Psychological aspects refer to the typical emotions and thoughts experienced by people who binge-eat. These can often be extremely distressing and are very powerful in maintaining the disordered eating. This section will explore four important psychological aspects related to binge-eating:

1 weight and shape concerns
2 typical emotions
3 common thinking errors
4 low self-esteem.

Weight and shape concerns

At the core of eating disorders are concerns about weight and shape. People often find themselves ruminating on their weight and shape, and this preoccupation can be a particularly distressing part of having an eating disorder.

There are several aspects of weight and shape concerns which are common to people with eating disorders:

- People who binge-eat often judge their self-worth largely, or exclusively, in terms of weight and shape. Indeed, to be diagnosed with bulimia nervosa your evaluations of yourself must be unduly influenced by body shape and weight.

- An intense fear of weight gain is common for people who have problems with their eating. This fear can be all-consuming, creating feelings of anxiety and panic, and can cause people to engage in damaging behaviours such as vomiting and severe dieting.
- Often people with eating disorders are very dissatisfied with their weight and shape. Usually, they feel that they weigh too much or that they are not thin enough. These thoughts can be very distressing and often, no matter how hard people try to block them out, the thoughts keep coming back. What we do know is that everyone tends to overestimate their body size and for people who have eating disorders this tendency is even more marked.

Typical emotions

There are some emotions that are particularly common for people who binge-eat. All these emotions are linked to each other and can often exacerbate an eating disorder. Emotions and binge-eating can interact to create vicious cycles which help maintain the eating problem; not only can emotions trigger an episode of bingeing, but the bingeing itself can intensify the emotion (Figure 2).

Some people binge-eat to help them control or block out their emotions. Occasionally, when people first stop bingeing their emotions can become more prominent. But this is transient, and facing

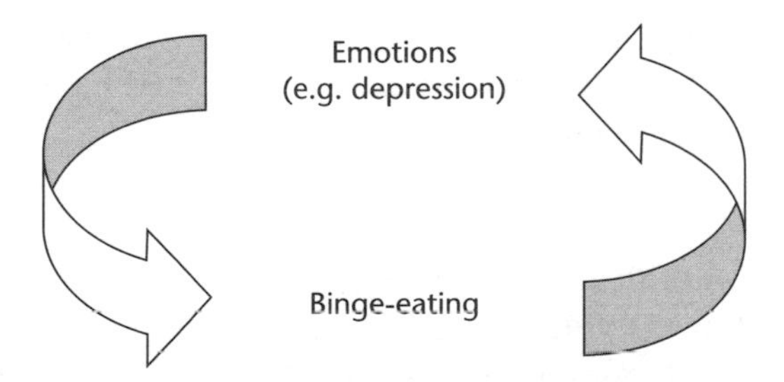

Figure 2 Binge-eating and emotions

the underlying emotion is an important step in overcoming your eating disorder. There are a number of very useful books which aim to address these emotions (see 'Further reading').

Low mood

Low mood is common in people who binge-eat. Indeed, for some, feelings of sadness, worthlessness and helplessness can develop into unmistakable depression. Often when people are depressed they experience a persistent lack of energy, poor memory and concentration and disturbed sleeping. They may also have feelings of guilt, may lose interest in things they previously found enjoyable and can feel empty inside.

Some people binge in response to feeling low. Often bingeing can help someone cope in the short term with feelings of depression. Unfortunately, the very fact that someone has given in to bingeing can lead to feelings of being helpless and worthless and thus the vicious cycle between depression and binge-eating is created.

Anxiety

It is very common for people to feel anxious before and after bingeing. This anxiety can cause people to worry, both about the eating disorder and about other aspects of their life. Anxiety also has a physical component; you may start to sweat, have hot flushes or chills, feel dizzy or faint, start shaking, have a racing heart, feel pressure in your chest or have problems breathing. All these symptoms of anxiety can be unpleasant and sometimes scary, but they are *not* harmful.

As with depression, some people binge-eat to help relieve themselves of the feelings of anxiety that can feel overwhelming. Again, this relief is short-lived, and thoughts about increases in weight or lack of control associated with the binge can cause a person's anxiety to increase again to unbearable levels.

Anger

Anger can be a difficult emotion to put into words and sometimes people find it hard to identify the feeling. But anger is a very prominent and often dominant emotion related to binge-eating. Feeling angry can often be very confusing and uncomfortable, especially if people have had negative experiences of anger being directed at them in the past. But it is common for anger to stem from the turmoil of having an eating disorder.

Shame and guilt

People often feel extremely guilty and ashamed after bingeing. These feelings can often feed into and intensify the other emotions discussed here. They can also create a desire to hide the eating disorder from other people. This secrecy can have incredibly damaging effects on relationships, even resulting in people isolating themselves from their friends and families for fear that their eating problems might be discovered.

Common thinking errors

It is very common for people to have certain errors in their thinking which can distort their perception of themselves, others and the world around them. These 'thinking errors' often become automatic and everyone has them from time to time. Certain thinking errors are especially common for people with eating disorders and can encourage binge-eating.

All-or-nothing thinking

All-or-nothing thinking is seeing things in black-and-white categories, or thinking in extremes. When people think in such extremes they are unable to see all the alternative options or views, and this can lead them to feel or behave in extreme ways. Here are some examples of all-or-nothing thinking:

- Certain foods are *either* good *or* bad.
- You think you are *either* in control *or* out of control.
- You think you can be *either* thin *or* fat.

Perfectionism, the desire to be perfect and setting excessively high standards for yourself, is very common in people with eating disorders. People who are perfectionists often think in all-or-nothing terms because anything less than excellence means failure.

All-or-nothing thinking can encourage bingeing as it can lead to having very strict dietary rules and 'giving up' and 'giving in to' bingeing when these often unattainable rules are broken.

Mental filter

People are said to be using a mental filter when they concentrate on negative details and ignore anything positive. For example, imagine a young woman, Sarah, is out shopping for jeans with a friend. The friend says she likes the way all the jeans look on Sarah, except one pair. If Sarah were to dwell on the fact that her friend said one pair was a little tight and feel anxious about her weight, ignoring the compliments her friend paid her, she would be using a mental filter. This would be a common reaction for someone with an eating disorder.

Emotional reasoning

Emotional reasoning is assuming that your negative emotions reflect the way things really are. It's important to remember that thoughts are different from facts: because we feel something does not mean it's true. For example, someone with an eating disorder may think: 'I feel fat, therefore I am fat,' or 'I feel out of control, therefore I have no control.'

Catastrophizing

Catastrophizing is overestimating the chances of disaster. For example, someone with an eating disorder may think that a weight increase of even a tiny amount means his or her weight will start to increase dramatically and spiral out of control, leading to certain disaster.

Mind reading

Mind reading is guessing what other people are thinking rather than asking them. For example, people with an eating disorder may think, 'My partner hasn't commented on how I look tonight. I must look awful.' Instead of checking with their partner, they may convince themselves that they look bad.

Low self-esteem

The majority of people with binge-eating disorders will have low self-esteem. Everything we have discussed so far in this chapter is linked to low self-esteem:

- People with eating disorders often base their self-worth primarily on their shape and weight. This can leave people very vulnerable to having their self-esteem threatened when something happens to their weight or shape; it's the equivalent of having all your eggs in one basket.
- Low self-esteem can be amplified by emotions. For example, when people are feeling low they tend to think negatively about themselves. Thoughts of inadequacy, failure and pessimism about the future are common to people who have low mood.
- Thinking errors can lower our self-esteem by distorting our perception of ourselves, reinforcing beliefs that 'we are no good'.

Summary

- Concerns about weight and shape are usually at the core of an eating disorder, and people can find preoccupations with these concerns particularly distressing.
- Certain emotions are often experienced by people who binge-eat – depression, anxiety, anger, shame and guilt. Often people binge-eat to help cope with these emotions in the short term; paradoxically, the emotions are often amplified by bingeing in the long term.
- Errors in the way someone thinks can help maintain disordered eating. A common error is all-or-nothing thinking, where people can see only in extremes (such as 'I think I can be *either* thin *or* fat').
- Most people who binge-eat have low self-esteem.

Behavioural aspects

As well as the psychological aspects of eating disorders, there are also behavioural aspects. These refer to some of the behaviours that people with eating disorders may carry out to influence their weight and shape. Common behaviours include dieting, vomiting, exercise and using laxatives. This chapter will describe these behaviours, focusing on their relationship to binge-eating and the consequences they have on the body.

Dieting

The majority of people with eating disorders diet in order to address the excessive concerns they have about their weight and shape. Dieting can refer to anything from cutting out particular types of food to a reduction in the overall amount that you eat. Many people diet after bingeing in an attempt to counteract any calories ingested. However, dieting itself can *cause* bingeing, as will be discussed next. Thus, a vicious cycle of dieting and bingeing is created (Figure 3).

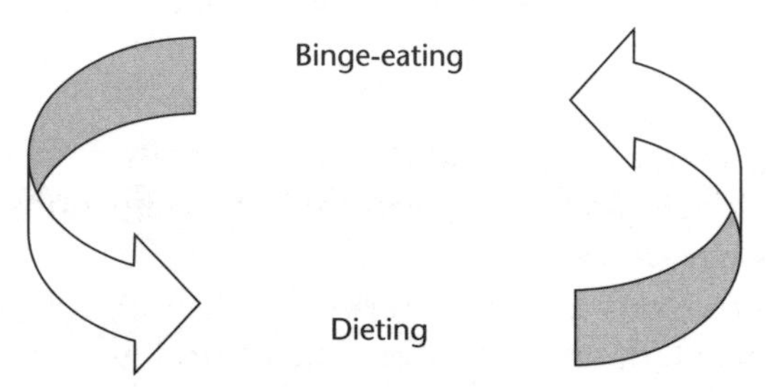

Figure 3 Binge-eating and dieting

Psychological consequences of dieting

- People who are dieting usually have a preoccupation with food and eating, and are unable to control intrusive thoughts about the very thing they are trying to avoid. Not only can these thoughts increase the chance that someone will binge, they can be very distressing and often result in an inability to concentrate at work, on conversations and other day-to-day activities.
- Diets are often governed by strict dietary rules. These rules are often unattainable; when they are broken, people often give up altogether on dieting and end up bingeing (this is an example of 'all-or-nothing thinking' described on p. 17).
- Dieting can affect your emotions. People tend to get irritable and short-tempered when their bodies are deprived of food. Dieting can also lead to low mood, feelings of anxiety and mood swings.
- Diets are ineffective; research shows that 95 per cent of people who go on a diet eventually put the weight back on, and often

more. As a result people who diet are often swinging between unrealistic restrictive eating patterns and periods of less controlled eating, usually not getting the results they desire. This yo-yoing can lead to feelings of failure and a sense they have no control, which can impact self-esteem.

Physiological consequences of dieting

- It is crucial to understand that dieting can directly result in bingeing. Depriving your body of food, and thus energy, causes a strong physiological pressure to eat. People can end up bingeing in a response to this powerful force.
- When you diet, your metabolism slows down in order to conserve the small amount of food available. This is an intelligent move on your body's part, and probably has helped people to survive in times of famine. The problem is that, when you stop dieting, since your metabolism has slowed down it becomes easier than ever to gain weight and you put weight on faster and more easily. Each time you go through another diet, this cycle continues. The only way to speed up your metabolism again is to eat.
- Dieting interferes with the natural mechanisms that control eating. We know that different types of food can influence our appetites (specifically carbohydrate, fat and protein). For example, carbohydrates suppress hunger. If you avoid carbohydrates you are denying yourself a natural appetite-suppressant.

Vomiting

For some people who binge-eat, vomiting becomes a way of 'compensating' for the food they consume during a binge. Vomiting can be seen as a way of 'regaining' control following a binge and a way of ridding the body of the calories consumed. Paradoxically, however, vomiting can also lead to an increase in binge-eating, weight gain and a loss of control.

- It has been estimated that 30–50 per cent of calories consumed during a binge are retained by the body after vomiting.
- Over time, as you continue to vomit, the body is able to find

ways of retaining more calories despite vomiting, meaning that vomiting becomes less and less effective as a means of controlling weight.

In addition, vomiting actually makes you more likely to binge:

- The body produces insulin when you binge in order to digest the food eaten. When you vomit, an excess of insulin is left in the bloodstream. This results in a low blood sugar level, causing your brain to think that the body is still hungry. Hence, you are at an increased risk of bingeing again shortly after having vomited.
- When people believe that they will be able to get rid of all the calories they eat during a binge, they actually become more likely to binge, since they imagine it will have no impact on their weight.

So, while people think that they may be consuming less food when they vomit, in the long run it is likely that vomiting will lead to an increase in the overall amount of calories consumed.

Vomiting also has many potentially dangerous or unwanted side effects, including:

- irregular heartbeat
- cardiac problems
- fatigue
- muscle weakness
- irritability
- dental erosion
- swollen salivary glands increasing the roundness of the face
- damage to the throat and throat infections
- tearing of the oesophagus.

Laxative use

Laxatives can be another way in which people attempt to 'cancel out' the effects of bingeing. However, laxatives work on the large bowel whereas calories are absorbed in the small bowel, earlier in the digestive system. This means that laxatives have very little impact on calorie absorption, getting rid of at most 12 per cent of calories each time they are used, no matter how many you use.

Like vomiting, laxative use can also have serious effects on the health:

- It lowers the levels of essential salts (potassium, sodium and chloride) in the body, which can cause potentially fatal cardiac problems.
- Long-term dehydration related to laxative use can also cause kidney failure and urinary tract infections.
- The body can also adapt to long-term use of laxatives, increasing its dependence on them, which makes reducing or stopping laxative use very difficult in later life.
- Long-term use may cause damage to the muscles of the bowel, resulting in anal incontinence which may require major surgery.

Excessive exercise

Excessive exercise is one of the diagnostic criteria for all eating disorders. It is estimated that around half of people with bulimia nervosa use exercise as a compensatory behaviour, i.e. to combat binge-eating. Excessive exercise is not necessarily about the amount of exercise you are doing – after all, we all know that exercise can be a healthy behaviour. However, it can become unhealthy, particularly when paired with disordered eating. Excessive exercise refers really to the type of exercise you are doing and how you feel about it. If you feel guilty after missing an exercise session, if you exercise in exactly the same way every time you exercise (exercise rigidity), if exercise has a 'driven' nature, if you continue to exercise despite illness or fatigue or if exercise gets in the way of other important life events or requirements, it is likely that your exercise may be problematic.

Excessive exercise when paired with eating problems, especially binge-eating, is associated with increased distress, more severe eating disorder symptoms and increased physical complications. It puts you at increased risk of injury, dehydration, exhaustion, poor concentration and osteoporosis (due to absent or reduced menstruation). In addition, as with vomiting, dieting and laxative use, believing you have a means of compensating for the calories consumed during a binge reduces the guilt associated with bingeing, therefore making it more likely to happen. Exercise will also increase hunger levels, therefore increasing the physiological urges to binge.

Summary

- The vast majority of people who binge-eat also diet, often to counteract the calories invested during a binge. However, dieting places psychological and physiological demands on the individual that actually increase the chance that he or she will binge again.
- Some people vomit after they have binged as a way of compensating for the food they have just consumed. What most people don't know is that vomiting is ineffective (with approximately 30–50 per cent of calories being retained by the body) and makes the individual more likely to binge. Vomiting is also a dangerous behaviour with a number of physical consequences.
- Laxative abuse is another way in which people attempt to rid themselves of the calories consumed in a binge. However, laxatives have little impact on calorie absorption and long-term use can have detrimental effects on the body.
- Finally, exercise, when paired with an eating disorder and done excessively, can be an unhealthy and unhelpful pursuit.

3

Social aspects

This chapter will look at how various aspects of our lives, such as our environment, personal relationships, work and how we spend our free time, all interact with an eating disorder.

Eating difficulties become most problematic when your focus on eating and weight starts to take over your life, pushing other, previous, interests or responsibilities to the outside. The pie charts in Figure 4 show how the importance of and time invested in different aspects of someone's life can be overshadowed by concerns about eating and body shape and size.

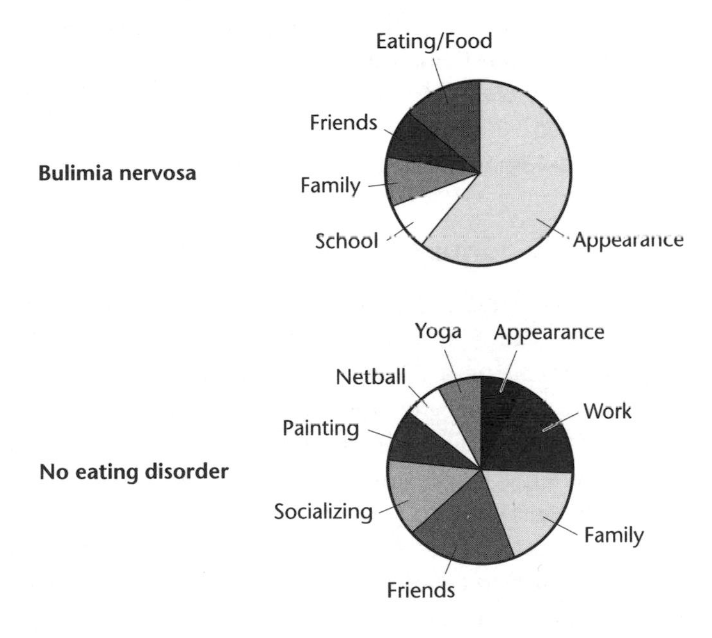

Figure 4 Comparison of amount of time invested in different aspects of life for individual with bulimia nervosa and individual with no eating disorder

Friends, family and intimate relationships

It is not uncommon for people to describe specific interpersonal events as being a trigger to bingeing, such as having an argument with a partner, being criticized by a parent or feeling ignored by a friend. Bingeing can help to take your mind off the difficulties you are experiencing in those relationships and act as a way of 'numbing' or 'releasing' the difficult emotions experienced as a result of these interpersonal events. Sometimes, when people first give up bingeing, their emotions may feel more intense or more difficult to cope with because for so long they have turned to bingeing in a response to these situations. However, it is possible to find alternative, less harmful strategies to cope with such emotions. Suggestions for alternative ways to cope with emotions are given in Part 2 of this book.

Binge-eating can also cause difficulties in relationships, or increase those due to changes in behaviour and mood.

- People can become very secretive about their eating, often lying to others about their behaviours.
- They may avoid seeing friends or going out if they know that food is involved.
- They may also lose interest in intimacy and sex.

Interests and work

Difficulties in work and sometimes certain personal interests can again be both a cause and a consequence of eating problems. Pressure at work can be a trigger to bingeing, again as a way of escaping or avoiding the emotions associated with this pressure. Eating disorders can also feed into difficulties in concentrating on tasks or with energy levels, motivation and enthusiasm, and in some cases may cause you to take time off work through illness.

It is worth noting that if you work in an industry which has a body focus (e.g. the fashion industry, media or fitness) this may also increase body image concerns and the amount you focus on your body.

Media

Over time, extreme standards of thinness for women have become widely accepted and have been 'marketed' ever more aggressively. These standards for a thin body shape have become increasingly unrealistic and destructive. Today's thin ideal is unrealistic for the majority of women. The body size of models is often more than 20 per cent underweight (exceeding the diagnostic criteria for anorexia nervosa of 15 per cent underweight).

Numerous studies have shown that exposure to images of thin women can increase body dissatisfaction. Studies have also shown that even very quick, flashed images can have a negative effect, so imagine what a lifetime of daily exposure can do to a woman's body esteem. And not just teenagers and women are vulnerable to media images. Children as young as five years old have been shown to be susceptible to an unrealistically thin body ideal. One study found that five- to eight-year-old girls reported lower body esteem and greater desire for a thinner body shape after being exposed to Barbie dolls. The *current* ideal body shape for women is closest to that of the prepubescent, immature girl's body. For most women, achieving this body shape would require losing so much body fat that it would become impossible to maintain normal menstrual functioning, normal libido (interest in sexual activity) and normal levels of reproductive hormones.

The fashion, diet and weight-loss industries are multi-million-pound trades, and while these industries continue to benefit financially from the promotion of these ideals they will go on marketing them even more strongly. The media are never the sole reason a person develops an eating disorder. However, it seems clear that the media are responsible for creating a toxic environment in which eating disorders are likely to flourish. More information is given about this later in this book.

Summary

- People who are battling with a binge-eating disorder often experience a change in their social environment. Secrecy about their eating problem can impact their relationships, and people can start avoiding social situations if they know food will be involved. Concerns about their body can also lead to a loss of interest in intimacy and sex.

- Food and concerns about weight can become so important to some people who binge-eat that they can overshadow other aspects of the person's life, like work and leisure activities.
- Research has shown that exposure to the thin ideal body shape portrayed in the media can increase body dissatisfaction.

4

Medical aspects

In the past several years, much research has been conducted examining the consequences of eating disorders, including bulimia nervosa. This section summarizes some of these findings.

Electrolyte disturbances

Electrolytes are salts in the body. They are essential for metabolic processes, for normal functioning of nerve and muscle cells, and for overall functioning of most organs including the heart, brain and kidneys. A large number of individuals with eating disorders have fluid or electrolyte abnormalities due to vomiting, laxative or diuretic abuse, or low salt intake and the resulting dehydration. Electrolyte disturbance is probably the most dangerous complication of vomiting and purgative abuse and can cause weakness, tiredness, constipation and depression; it can result in cardiac arrhythmias and sudden death. If you are vomiting regularly, it is important to check that your electrolyte levels are within a normal range, something you can do via a simple blood test at your GP surgery. Abnormalities in electrolyte levels can be corrected for a brief period with salt supplements, which your GP can also prescribe.

Cardiac irregularities

Many of the deaths in all eating disorders, including bulimia nervosa, are the consequences of cardiac irregularities. The combined effect of restriction and electrolyte disturbances (caused by purging behaviours) may result in serious irregularities in the heartbeat. This is particularly so during exercise and may be associated with sudden death. Irregularities are detectable by electrocardiograph (ECG, or heart monitor), and are often experienced as palpitations (rapid, and often irregular, heartbeat).

Cardiac irregularities can also occur as a result of ingesting some purgatives, such as certain laxatives or emetics (substances which induce vomiting). Your GP can carry out an ECG if you are experiencing any of these symptoms.

Dental problems

Many individuals who self-induce vomiting notice marked deterioration in their teeth. Tooth colour may change from white to brown or grey, and complications may require extensive dental work or even removal of the teeth.

When vomiting is induced, as well as the recently eaten food other gastric substances, including stomach acids, are brought into the mouth. This highly acidic mixture is responsible for general dental erosion and loss of enamel (decalcification), resulting in decay and periodontal disease. Increased sensitivity to temperature is also common. The dental problems found in many individuals with eating disorders are generally not reversed with a return to normal eating.

In order to limit some of the damage to teeth enamel if you are vomiting, it is advisable to use a non-acid mouth wash or fluoride toothpaste. Rinsing your mouth out with water after vomiting and delaying brushing your teeth for a couple of hours will also help to protect your teeth from erosion and acid decay. It is essential to visit your dentist regularly.

Gastrointestinal complications

Abdominal pain is common in individuals with eating disorders. This may be directly related to bingeing and vomiting. Many individuals with eating disorders are diagnosed with irritable bowel syndrome, which is generally considered to be a direct result of the eating disorder behaviours, and these symptoms do tend to improve with a reduction in the behaviours. In severe cases, very large binges can also result in pancreatitis or stretching of the stomach, which may result in a fatal tearing or rupture of the stomach. Repeated self-induced vomiting may lead to serious tearing of tissue in the mouth and throat. Choking on vomit can occur.

Laxative abuse can cause constipation, especially when you first stop using laxatives. Usually bowel functioning returns to normal with normal eating. However, in rare cases permanent impairment of bowel functioning can occur due to degeneration of nerve cells in the bowel, and surgery may be required. Extensive laxative abuse may cause bloody diarrhoea.

Individuals who diet regularly have a general reduction in the activity of the bowel. This can cause delays in stomach-emptying (and can prolong the sense of fullness after a meal) and slowing of other bowel activity. Reduced bowel activity may actually proceed to a total paralysis of the bowel. Constipation is common, as a result of reduced bowel activity and dehydration. Gastrointestinal bleeding, ulcers and difficulty absorbing certain foods are also common.

Oedema and dehydration

Purging (by vomiting, or abusing laxatives or diuretics) and strict dieting (by restricting food and fluid intake) often result in dehydration and lead to 'rebound' excessive water retention. Dehydration is signalled by extreme thirst and reduced urinary output. Sometimes swelling or puffiness in the fingers, ankles or face indicates water retention. Usually the water retention is worst after stopping using laxatives or after vomiting, and can contribute as much as 4.5 kg of 'water weight'. The wide swings between dehydration and water retention gradually reduce once the individual stops purging and begins to eat regularly. However, water retention can be so alarming, because of the associated weight gain and puffiness, that many individuals return to vomiting or laxative abuse before their bodies have had a chance to achieve balance, and this starts the cycle all over again.

Excessive water retention may also be related to low protein intake, excessive periods of time spent standing, and bingeing on large quantities of salty foods.

Neurological abnormalities

Abnormal electrical discharges in the brain are common in some individuals with eating disorders. Epileptic seizures have been reported in a proportion of cases of bulimia nervosa, and muscular spasms and tingling sensations in the extremities (peripheral paraesthesia) also occur. Some of these are due to vitamin and mineral deficiencies.

Brain scans have shown abnormalities in the size of the ventricles (fluid-filled spaces among the brain matter) and the structural organization of the brain, and there is evidence that certain types of information processing may be affected in individuals with eating disorders.

Kidney dysfunction

Kidney disturbances occur in some individuals with eating disorders and are probably related to low levels of the electrolyte potassium. This may result in a susceptibility to urinary tract infection. Kidney damage is rare, but has been reported in some individuals with eating disorders.

Endocrine abnormalities

Many women with eating disorders develop irregularities in their menstrual cycle, including amenorrhoea (absence of menstrual periods). This is very likely to be related to loss of body fat, but other factors may also play a role, including dysfunction of the hypothalamus (a small area at the base of the brain).

Dermatological changes

The skin is extremely sensitive to nutritional change. Many individuals with eating disorders, especially those with low weight, have dry, cracking skin, which is probably related to dehydration and to the loss of subcutaneous fat (the layer of fat just below the skin) as well as deficiencies of certain vitamins, such as vitamins A and E. Self-induced vomiting often causes the skin around the mouth to become red and irritated. Often fingernails and toenails will become brittle and break easily. Hands and feet may take on a bluish colour, due to an excessive amount of reduced haemoglobin in the blood. Bingeing and vomiting may also result in broken blood vessels in the face, mouth or eyes.

Often individuals with eating disorders experience swelling of the parotid glands (in front of or below the ears). This is usually not painful, but is noticeable as 'puffy cheeks'. It is not clear why this swelling occurs, although it has been speculated that it may be related to electrolyte disturbances, physical irritation of the glands through vomiting, endocrine (hormonal) dysfunction or nutritional deficiencies. It may persist for several months after a return to normal eating.

Mood and personality

Starvation frequently leads to changes in the individual's personality. Mood changes are common, with rapid shifts from depression to elation. Many individuals who are starved or semi-starved report feeling irritable and short-tempered. Obsessive thoughts (often, but not always, about food) and compulsive behaviours are not uncommon.

Cognition

Many starved individuals display impaired concentration and alertness. Often this results in feeling distractible, apathetic and lethargic. For many individuals who induce their own starvation, the restriction represents being in control, and the starvation-induced impairment in concentration is often so distressing that they further starve to feel more in control, thus worsening the cognitive symptoms.

Sleep

Starvation or semi-starvation frequently results in insomnia, despite feelings of tiredness and lethargy. In particular, early morning awakening is common. There is some evidence of changes in the pattern of brain waves during sleep in starved individuals. These changes are usually reversed once normal eating has resumed.

Fertility

There is a lot of research that has looked into the effects of having an eating disorder on the reproductive system, menstruation, ovarian function, pregnancy, fertility and sexuality. These effects are both physical and emotional in nature. Below, we have listed some of the more negative consequences of having an eating disorder on these areas.

Research has shown that around one in five people who suffer from bulimia will have difficulties getting pregnant, as a result of problems with ovulation. Over half of women with bulimia will have problems with their menstrual cycle: that is, they will have fewer or even no periods. This is due to abnormalities in the hormones that regulate menstruation caused by the continued use of bulimic behaviours. It results in increased difficulties in getting pregnant; however, even women who are having regular periods report difficulties conceiving, which may well result from the use of bulimic behaviours.

There is an increased likelihood of polycystic ovary syndrome (PCOS), a condition in which there are a number of small harmless cysts around the edge of the ovaries. These cysts contain undeveloped follicles which do not release any eggs, hence the difficulties in getting pregnant. Alongside increased difficulties becoming pregnant, symptoms that tend to be associated with this condition include irregular periods, weight gain, acne and excessive hair growth. It is not yet clear why this condition occurs more frequently in women with bulimia; however, it is clear that both dieting and bingeing are likely to perpetuate PCOS.

During pregnancy, there may also be many difficulties that can be linked to having bulimia nervosa. These difficulties include increased miscarriage rates, preterm delivery, low infant birth weight and birth complications. There is also some evidence to suggest higher blood pressure and higher rates of depression in mothers with bulimia nervosa. Individuals with bulimia nervosa lack micro- and macro-nutrients, especially vitamins (for example, vitamins A and D, iron, zinc, folic acid) which are all important to successful pregnancies and birth. To reduce the changes of experiencing all of these difficulties, it is important to ensure an adequate intake of each of the major food groups both before and during pregnancy.

Women with bulimia tend to be more sexually active than those with anorexia nervosa. However, their sexual behaviour and sexual interest usually varies together with fluctuations in body weight and eating behaviours. In some women with bulimia nervosa there is an increased incidence of impulsivity, which can include impulsive sexual behaviour. As a result there may also be an increased risk of unwanted pregnancy and sexually transmitted disease. In addition, when people are vomiting as well as bingeing, contraceptives such as the pill are likely to be much less effective.

5

Understanding your eating disorder: a self-assessment

The very fact that you are reading this book probably indicates that you think you have a problem with binge-eating (or perhaps you fear that a loved one has such a problem).

It is often very hard for people who binge-eat to be honest with themselves about the extent of their disorder and it is common to feel a range of emotions when you start to face up to your difficulties. However, hard as it can be, acknowledging and understanding your problems with eating is an essential part of overcoming them.

Over the next chapter, you will be guided through a series of exercises which will help you explore and understand your eating disorder in more detail.

There are three aspects of binge-eating which will be important for you to understand:

1. *Knowledge of the history of your eating problem*: this allows you to see how events in the past have affected your eating. Understanding these connections can help you to prevent certain events affecting your eating in the future and, as such, it is important to closely explore these links.
2. *Knowing when you are most vulnerable to bingeing*: this will help you pre-empt those times when you would be likely to binge, an essential part of avoiding bingeing altogether.
3. *Awareness of the extent of your binge-eating problem*: this enables you to see if the severity of your problem changes. You will be able to see if there have been improvements in your eating and if the programme is working for you. On the other hand, you will be able to highlight when things are getting worse and action needs to be taken.

Exercise 1: Mapping the history of your binge-eating problem

This step-by-step exercise helps you create a timeline for your eating problems, with attention to major events in your life and changes in your weight.

Figure 5 illustrates this exercise with the case of Joanna, a 26-year-old female who has a ten-year history of bulimia nervosa.

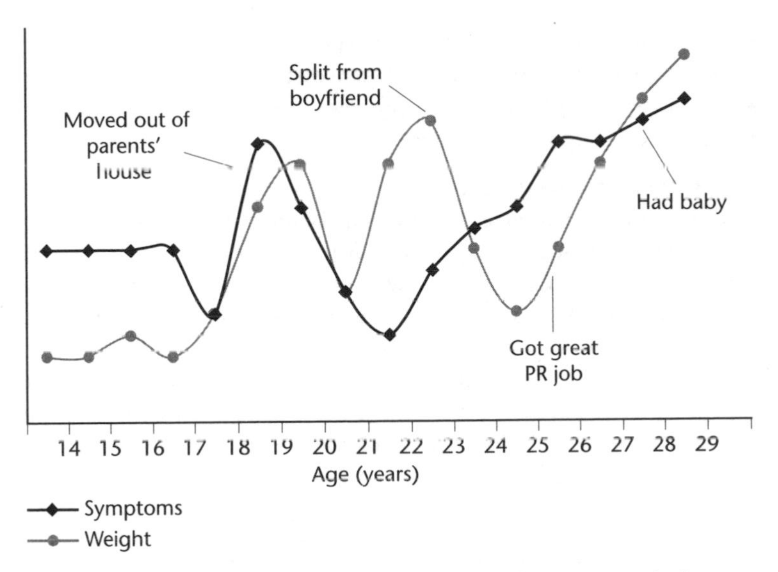

Figure 5 Joanna's timeline, showing severity of symptoms in her binge-eating disorder in relation to life events

The history of your eating problem

Step 1: Create a timeline

Using a whole piece of paper (at least A4 size) copy the timeline in Figure 5, marking your age on the horizontal axis.

Step 2: Draw your symptoms line

The next stage is to draw a line on the chart to show how the severity of your symptoms has changed over time. For this exercise, your symptoms refer to your binge-related behaviours (bingeing, vomiting and use of laxatives; please see Chapter 2 for more detail on these behaviours).

It can be difficult to recall precisely how your symptoms have changed over the years. You will be very unlikely to get it exactly right; instead, concentrate on getting a general idea of when your symptoms have been better and when they have been worse.

Mark the severity of your symptoms on the chart at the following key points to help guide your symptoms line:

- when your problem with eating began;
- when your symptoms were at their worst;
- times your symptoms have improved;
- how your symptoms are now.

Step 3: Draw your weight line

As discussed in Chapter 2, people with binge-eating disorders nearly always have significant concerns about their weight. Seeing how your weight has changed, or indeed stayed the same, can often provide you with important information about how your weight has or hasn't been affected by your binge-related behaviours.

Using a different colour pen, draw a line on the chart to show how your weight has fluctuated over the years. Like the symptoms line, this can be difficult to do. To help, mark on the chart the following key points to guide your line:

- your lowest adult weight;
- your highest adult weight;
- for women only, your weight when your periods began;
- your weight when your symptoms began;
- your weight now.

Step 4: Mark significant life events on your chart

Next, mark on your chart any important events in your life. These can be anything that has happened in your life that *you* consider to be important and to have affected you in some way. The example of Joanna illustrates how this can be done, with the following important events in her life:

- moved out of parents' house;
- split up from first boyfriend;

- got great PR job;
- had a baby.

Step 5: Making the connections between symptoms, weight and life events
The final stage of this exercise is to spend some time thinking about how the three aspects of your chart are connected – your symptoms, your weight and your significant life events. For example, Joanna's chart illustrates how after she split up with her boyfriend she lost some weight, but soon after that her bingeing increased. Sometimes connections can jump out at you and seem obvious, but sometimes they can be very hard to spot; it is worth revisiting your chart throughout the programme as links may become apparent later on. And, of course, sometimes there simply are no connections. Everyone's history is different; some people find this much easier than others and you shouldn't worry if you cannot make the connections – it certainly doesn't mean you cannot use this programme.

Exercise 2: Exploring when you are vulnerable to bingeing

This exercise will help you think about when you are most vulnerable to bingeing; knowing when you are likely to binge is a powerful weapon for tackling your binge-eating. It allows you to pre-empt the binges, and in turn you can use certain techniques to avoid them (these techniques will be discussed in subsequent chapters).

We have illustrated this exercise with the case of Jackie, a 32-year-old woman whose weekly binges are affecting her confidence, which in turn is having an impact on her relationship with her partner.

Your binge-eating profile

Step 1: Draw your binge-eating profile
Draw out your own binge-eating profile table like Jackie's in Table 1 overleaf.

Step 2: The questions

Below is a list of questions, one for each of the rows in your binge-eating profile. Spend some time thinking about each of the questions and fill your answers into your table.

Some of these questions may be very easy for you to answer. Others may be much more difficult, and indeed some might not be applicable to you at all. Often, as people move through the programme, they think of new and different answers to these questions, so it is important to revisit your binge-eating profile.

- *When?* Is there a time of day when you are most likely to binge?
- *Where?* Are there certain places where you are more likely to binge?
- *Who?* Are you more likely to binge before or after seeing certain people?
- *What?* Are you more likely to binge before or after certain events or activities?
- *Feelings?* How do you feel before you binge?
- *Food?* What foods do you binge on?

There are no right or wrong answers; everyone's binge-eating profile is unique!

Table 1 Jackie's binge-eating profile

When?	Sunday evenings
Where?	My kitchen
Who?	Before I have to see my boss on Monday
What?	Before I have to face the working week
Feelings?	Very anxious
Food?	Ice cream

Exercise 3: Measuring the extent of your eating problems using a quick assessment guide

The assessment guide that follows is designed to provide you with a quick and easy look at the extent of your binge-eating. Being able to measure the extent of your bingeing is a very useful tool; it allows you to see when things are improving, which can show you what is helping you overcome your binge-eating. It also allows you to see when things are getting worse, when you might need to take more action. We recommend that you copy out this assessment guide and complete it weekly while you are using this programme.

Quick assessment guide (Bamford and Brown)

1 How many times in the last month have you binged? ☐
  (a) How many of these were objective binges (excessive amount of food and a sense of loss of control)? ☐
  (b) How many of these were subjective binges (small or normal amount of food and a sense of loss of control)? ☐

2 How many times in the last month have you vomited as a way of controlling your weight or shape? ☐

3 How many times have you used laxatives as a way of controlling your shape or weight? ☐

4 How often has your binge-eating resulted in you feeling bad about yourself?

Never	Rarely	Sometimes	Often	Always
☐	☐	☐	☐	☐

5 How often has your binge-eating caused you physical complaints?

Never	Rarely	Sometimes	Often	Always
☐	☐	☐	☐	☐

6 How often has your binge-eating reduced your ability to concentrate?

Never	Rarely	Sometimes	Often	Always
☐	☐	☐	☐	☐

7 How often has your binge-eating caused you financial concerns?

Never	Rarely	Sometimes	Often	Always
☐	☐	☐	☐	☐

8 How often does your binge-eating affect your work or schooling?

Never	Rarely	Sometimes	Often	Always
☐	☐	☐	☐	☐

9 How often does your binge-eating affect relationships or friendships?

Never	Rarely	Sometimes	Often	Always
☐	☐	☐	☐	☐

Part 2
PSYCHOLOGICAL TREATMENT PROGRAMMES

By now you should be starting to have an understanding of some of the factors that may have contributed to the start of your eating disorder, some of the factors that may be maintaining your eating disorder, and the way you feel about your eating disorder at the moment. Part 2 of this book will take you through a guided recovery programme, the aim of which is to help you to gain control over your eating, to stop bingeing and vomiting, and to teach you skills that may help you to deal with difficulties in your life in a healthy way.

There is no set timeframe during which you should aim to work through this section. Recovery from an eating disorder is complex, often slow and quite likely to entail a number of setbacks and lapses. It is important that you do not expect to be free of bingeing immediately and that you allow yourself time and patience to deal with the ups and downs of your own recovery. Throughout this treatment section, we have included case studies, advice and ideas about how to deal with typical stumbling blocks. In case this is not enough, however, we have also included guidance and details about where you might be able to seek further professional help.

The treatment programme outlined in this book is based on ideas taken from cognitive behavioural theory (CBT). Very simply, cognitive behavioural therapy looks at the **thoughts** you have about yourself, others and your eating; the **feelings** you experience; your **behaviours**; and the ways in which all three interact to maintain your eating disorder. For example, people often start dieting (a behaviour) to overcome low self-esteem or negative thoughts about themselves (cognitions). Dieting, for the reasons that were outlined on pages 20–1, can often trigger overeating or bingeing, which can further decrease self-esteem and negative thoughts about oneself. People also often report using bingeing as a way of reducing strong negative emotions they feel unable to manage. Cognitive behavioural theory tries to explore each of these aspects and provide you with skills which can help you to change or cope with your thoughts, feelings and behaviours, including dieting and bingeing. This programme will take you through how to change your eating in order to stop bingeing, as well as ways to cope with negative thoughts and feelings that you may have about yourself.

6

Getting started

Before you start to make changes to your eating, it is important to think about why you want to make these changes and to prepare yourself fully for them. This section of the book will ask you to think about the pros and cons of living with your eating disorder, the impact of your eating disorder on your life, possible barriers to change and possible sources of support. It is a good idea, before you start this programme, to buy yourself a notebook to record your thoughts, feelings and exercises throughout your treatment.

Task 1: Pros and cons of the eating disorder

In your notebook, start to make a list of the pros and cons of your eating disorder as you see them. For the Cons list, think about things that might have changed in your life since your eating disorder started, how your eating disorder makes you feel and the physical impact of your eating disorder, as well as the impact that your eating disorder may have on others around you. For the Pros list, think about why your eating disorder is important to you, what it does for you and what you fear may happen if you start to make changes. An example of this is given in Table 2. When you are happy with these lists, have a think about the importance to you of each of the things you have written and how much your eating disorder really helps or hinders in each of these areas.

Table 2 Pros and cons of my eating disorder

Pros	*Cons*
• It helps me to feel in control • It helps me to control my weight • I feel better about myself when I diet • I can release difficult emotions • It reduces the level of emotions I feel • Eating provides comfort but I don't have to deal with the consequences • I feel I can hide behind it	• I don't like the way I feel after I binge • I find it difficult to concentrate on anything because I'm thinking about food all the time • I find it difficult to go out with my friends if they are eating out, and this makes me feel isolated • I feel tired a lot of the time • I feel ashamed of myself because of my behaviour around food • I feel embarrassed that people know I have an eating disorder • I am not as productive at work as I could be • I don't sleep very well • It makes me difficult to be in a relationship with anyone

Task 2: Deciding to change

Next, it may be useful to start to think about the impact changing your eating will have on your life. It can be helpful to break this down into short-term and long-term consequences, as in Table 3. Again, it is likely that you will predict both positive and negative consequences of change. It may help you to imagine what life will be like in one, five or ten years' time if you decide to change or if you choose to stay the same. Remember that bingeing does not just stop without you taking action. Unless you decide to change, it is very likely that your behaviours will continue and probably get worse.

Table 3 The impact of changing my eating

	Short-term consequences	*Long-term consequences*
If I decide to make changes to my eating	• I may feel more anxious • My weight may increase • I may not be able to cope with my emotions	• I don't know what this will be like, which is scary • It may be really good, but it may not be as good as I hope
If I decide not to make any changes to my eating	• Nothing will change • I will continue to feel ashamed and embarrassed • I won't feel well	• My bingeing may get worse • My family will worry more • My friends may get fed up and stop caring • I will make myself ill and risk serious illness • I may feel worse than I do now

Task 3: Possible barriers

Many people feel very anxious about changing any aspect of their eating. Below is a list of possible barriers to change that other people have described.

- Fear of weight gain.
- Fear of losing control over my life.
- Fear of losing others close to me (if they stop worrying or being concerned about me or if I gain weight).
- Fear of not being able to cope with the emotions I may feel if I do not binge.
- Fear of not being able to change.
- Fear of the unknown. (Who will I be or what will I do if I do change?)
- Fear of being unable to cope with life or responsibility without controlling eating or bingeing.
- Fear of having nothing left in my life.

Have a think about what your barriers or fears might be. Write each of these fears down in your notebook. Some common barriers are discussed next. However, if you feel that your specific barrier is not mentioned here, ask yourself:

- How likely is it that my fear will come true?
- How do I know this fear will come true (what is the evidence)?
- Does the possibility that it may come true mean that it is not worth trying to change?

The case studies on pages 50–1 may also help you to think about this.

Possible barrier 1: Fear of weight gain

Often, people's biggest fear when giving up bingeing or vomiting is that they will gain weight. This is hardly ever the case. The reason for this is that people usually consume more calories when they are bingeing than they would be if they were able to stick to a healthy meal plan. In addition, as discussed on pages 21–2, extreme methods of weight control are in fact very ineffective. Self-induced vomiting, for example, only gets rid of about 30 per cent of calories consumed, while laxatives get rid of at most 10 per cent. These behaviours also tend to increase the risk of bingeing, both because they make it psychologically more acceptable to binge and because physiologically these behaviours cause the body to want to eat more. As such, it is very rare for people who manage to stop bingeing and vomiting to weigh any more than they did prior to stopping.

Possible barrier 2: Fear of losing control

People often believe that controlling their eating is the only way they can feel in control over an aspect of their life. However, the reality is likely to be quite different.

- How much control do you really feel you have over your eating?
- How easy is it to 'just stop' bingeing?
- How much control does your eating disorder really help you have over other areas of your life?

The likelihood is that your eating disorder is actually controlling you at the moment and possibly even reducing the control you have over other areas of your life. The case study on page 50 describes Sarah's experience of this.

Possible barrier 3: Fear of having an empty life

Many people worry that without the amount of time they spend thinking about, eating or worrying about food, there will be little else for them to do or think about. Usually, people have no problem filling the increased time by thinking about other things, taking up new or previous interests and spending more time focusing on their relationships or friendships. Occasionally, however, if you are particularly worried about this, it can be useful to think about things that you want to start doing or ideas you have about how to fill the increased time that you are likely to have (these can be included in your 'goal list' – see Task 4).

Possible barrier 4: Fear of no longer having a way of coping with emotions

Making changes to your eating and stopping bingeing and vomiting can often be uncomfortable, and occasionally distressing. Often it is not quite as distressing as people predict and tends to become a lot easier fairly quickly. It can be useful, however, if you feel this is likely to be a problem for you, to make a list of ways to deal with these distressing experiences. Think about ways that you have managed emotions before, or things that your friends do to help them cope with emotions. It is not possible to avoid these emotions altogether but it is often a lot easier to manage them than people expect. Box 1 may give you a few ideas of different ways to manage emotions.

Box 1 Ways to cope with emotions

- Talk to others about them.
- Write them down.
- Do something you enjoy.
- Do something nice for yourself.
- Do some gentle exercise.
- Think about something positive that is happening or might happen in your life.
- Think about how you will feel in one day, one week or one year about the situation.

- Remind yourself, 'I'm going to be okay' and 'I'm not crazy; this is a normal part of the recovery process'.
- Listen to loud music or your favourite music.
- Distract yourself with a film or book.
- Stay in touch with people – don't isolate yourself.
- Go for a walk.

Sarah

Sarah started bingeing around the time that she went to university. When she got to university she found that a lot of her peers focused heavily on appearance, and everyone seemed to be constantly dieting. The demands of university assignments as well as her concerns over whether she would be able to make new friends combined to make Sarah highly anxious. Soon after she started uni, she started dieting in order to fit in with her peers. She found that focusing on her weight helped her to forget her anxiety about her course work and, indeed, at first seemed to help her to feel more in control of her academic work. However, when Sarah started bingeing this rapidly gave way to her feeling completely out of control and even more anxious. She used her food restriction as a way of regaining the sense of control she felt in the early stages of her eating disorder.

Sarah desperately wanted to stop the bingeing, but feared that stopping her restriction would result in her not only feeling out of control but actually being out of control, since she would no longer have a way of achieving the sense of control the restriction gave her. This, she believed, would surely mean that she would start to lose control over all parts of her life.

Lisa

Lisa had always used food as a way of escaping from distressing emotions. For as long as she could remember she had indulged in sweets or chocolates in order to make herself feel better. Lisa's mum was the same, and so to some extent Lisa had learned that the way to feel better was to eat things she enjoyed. As Lisa got older this behaviour became more pronounced. Lisa had turned to food after almost every difficult time in her life: splitting up with her boyfriend, failing her exams at school, moving to a new area. This had resulted in her weight fluctuating dramatically over the years, a fact that had made her feel even worse about herself. Gradually, Lisa had started to use food to 'escape' from almost any emotion she experienced. She enjoyed the sense of excitement and elation that eating large amounts of food gave her, and found that she could forget about anything else that was happening in her life when she was doing this.

As she started to do it more and more often, however, she became aware of the detrimental effect bingeing was starting to have on her life. She started to hate the weight she had gained as a result of the eating, and she became more and more isolated as she withdrew from her friends, fearful that they would find out about her eating. She started to feel more and more ashamed and guilty of her secret eating, and this only served to push her further into her secret eating binges as a way of escaping these horrendous feelings. Lisa longed to be able to give up her secret eating but feared no longer being able to eat the foods she so enjoyed. In the absence of any healthy ways of coping with emotions, she became petrified by the idea of actually having to experience and cope with her emotions and dreaded the thought of not being able to escape or shut out the horrendous emotions she knew she would experience if she tried to give up her bingeing.

Jessica

Jessica, 22, has always taken great pride in her appearance, focusing on her image and body from an early age. She has never been totally satisfied with her weight or shape and became very preoccupied with food from an early age. Jessica has a restrictive eating pattern throughout the day; however, when she gets back from work she binges on a large selection of foods she buys on the way home. Throughout the day her focus and thoughts revolve around what food she will purchase on this journey home, often impairing her ability to concentrate on her job and work efficiently and meaning she has little time in her day for her family and friends. Jessica has little else fulfilling in her life other than her thoughts around food; she feels nobody will understand and so does not want to share these thoughts. Thanks to such preoccupations Jessica does not have any close friends in her life; she does not have the time to keep in contact with people and feels she needs to keep her binges and thoughts secret. She is worried about getting treatment for her eating disorder, as although she wants to spend less time thinking about food and revolving her day around it, she does not know how her life would be without these thoughts and feelings. She is scared of being lonely and of having time to think about having nothing fulfilling in her life other than her current preoccupations with food.

Remember

Remember these are normal fears when contemplating change. There are ways of overcoming them. Try not to let the fear of what 'might' happen stop you from trying.

Task 4: Setting goals

By now, you have probably started to get a good idea of what, when and why you want to change. It is likely, if you have chosen to read this book, that you are contemplating making some changes to your eating. However, there may also be other things that you feel you need to change in order to help yourself to overcome your eating disorder: for example, feeling more comfortable eating in public or improving your view of your body. It is important to think about what your specific goals are. Use the guide in Box 2 to help you to choose appropriate, specific, achievable goals, and write your goals down near the beginning of your notebook so that you can keep referring back to them. It may also be useful to write down why you want to change each of these things. This will help you if you ever feel like giving up or can't remember why you wanted to change.

Box 2 Goal-setting

Before writing down your goals, consider the following points about goal-setting:

- Try to avoid having general, vague goals. Goals should be specific, measurable and realistic. Rather than writing 'To feel happier', for example, think about what might make you happier, such as 'To go out with friends more' or 'To get a new job', and make these your goals.
- Try to avoid setting goals that are beyond your control or are related to another person, such as 'For my sister to be nicer to me'.
- Only set goals that you or others would think are achievable: for example, 'To start an acting class' rather than 'To become a film star'.
- Try to break larger goals down into a number of smaller steps. For example, 'To get a new job' might be broken down into 'To look

at the job website', 'To update my CV' and 'To ask a friend to look over my application form'.

- Try to avoid setting yourself too many goals, as this may feel overwhelming. Remember that you can always move on to other goals once you have achieved the goals that feel most important to you now.
- If a large number of your goals feel equally important, it may be useful to think about which feel the easiest to achieve and to start with these easier ones first.
- Achieving goals often requires patience and persistence. Try not to give up on goals, or to change your goals drastically, before you have allowed yourself enough time to achieve them. For example, as we said earlier, stopping binge-eating can be a slow and frustrating experience. Just because you have not managed it immediately does not mean that it is impossible or that you will never achieve it.
- Try to choose goals that you *want* to achieve rather than goals that you feel you *should* achieve or that other people want you to achieve. Make sure you fully understand why you want to achieve them and what you expect the benefits of achieving them may be before you embark on any change.

Important: It is not appropriate to have 'To lose weight' as a goal. It is not possible to stop bingeing if you are trying to lose weight, and it is therefore essential that you accept for the time being you cannot diet. It is possible for some people to focus on losing weight in the future, once their binge-eating is under control.

Task 5: Seeking appropriate support

If you have got to the end of this chapter and still want to change, you are probably ready to move on to the next step. Before you do this, however, take a few minutes to think about who will be able to support you with this programme. You may have already told someone, or maybe many people, about your eating disorder, or you may feel too anxious or ashamed to talk to anyone about it. Have a think about whether you feel able to tell anyone, or who you might trust enough to ask to support you. If you do not feel able to talk to friends or family about your eating, you may feel able to go to your GP. Failing this, you will find a list of useful support-line numbers in the 'Useful addresses' section at the end of this book where you will be able to confide in expert, trained counsellors about how you are feeling.

Possible stumbling blocks?

I'm not sure if I'm ready

It is very common for people to feel anxious and uncertain about change. Think about times when you have decided to make other changes in your life and ask yourself:

- What did I decide to do then?
- Was this the right decision?
- Will I ever feel 100 per cent ready?
- If I decide not to change because I do not yet feel 100 per cent ready, how will I feel in one year's time when things are still the same?

I don't know if I can change

Admittedly, overcoming an eating disorder can sometimes be very difficult. However it is often not as difficult as people expect. While this book may not work for everyone, you will not know whether it works for you unless you try it. If, in the final analysis, it has not been successful, there is a list of alternative treatment options and contact numbers at the end of the book.

I don't know what it would involve

It is very common for people to feel extremely anxious about what changing will involve and who they will be if they do change. However, you will not know exactly what it will involve or what will happen unless you try it. Deciding to change, as with any decision, involves a small degree of risk. Ask yourself how you will feel in a year if you do not decide to take this risk.

I'm not sure if I really want to change

People feel ready to make changes to an eating disorder at different times, often living with their eating disorder for years before they feel ready to change. Only you can decide whether or not you want to do it now and what the consequences of deciding not to change will be. If you decide you do not feel ready now, it may be that you need to come back to this book at a later time. Remember, however, that the longer you have had an eating disorder, the greater its impact on your life will be, and the harder it will be to then make changes.

When to move on to the next step

Move on to the next step when you feel ready to make changes to your eating. If you are still not sure about whether to move on, reread the possible stumbling blocks that outline common barriers that other people have described when initiating self-help treatments. It may be useful for you to refer back, throughout the next few weeks or months, to what you have written in your notebook for the tasks in this chapter and think about whether anything you have written has changed.

Remember

Throughout your treatment programme, go back to your quick assessment questionnaire (see page 41). Completing this will help you keep track of your progress throughout your treatment and will also help you recognize when things might be getting worse. As a guideline, you should be completing this approximately every week to get an idea of how you are getting on.

7

Record-keeping

Why does bingeing happen?

As we said in Chapter 2, bingeing occurs because of a combination of emotional factors (such as feeling anxious) and physiological factors (such as the body's response to restriction or dieting). It is therefore important to look at both of these factors in order to stop bingeing. It is often easiest to deal with the physiological factors first so that you can start to be more aware of the emotional factors; if you take away all the binges that occur through hunger or starvation, it is a lot easier to be aware of the context in which emotional binges are happening. The remainder of this book tries to help you to address both the hunger-driven and emotion-driven binges.

The first task in changing your eating is to start monitoring your eating. To do this, you will need to record in your notebook everything that you eat and drink throughout the day, what time it was eaten or drunk, and whether you used any behaviours such as vomiting or laxative use. It can also be useful to have a separate column to jot down any thoughts or feelings you have about what you have eaten. All this can feel like a very daunting thing to do, but it is a *very* important part of change. Keeping a food diary will:

1 help you to face up to the reality of your current eating;
2 help you to make links between your experiences, thoughts, feelings and behaviours;
3 help you to understand better why your bingeing is happening.

It is very unlikely that you will be able to make to make any significant changes without recording everything you are eating and drinking during the day.

An example of a completed food diary is shown in Table 4. You can either draw it in your therapy notebook or buy a separate, smaller notebook just for your food diary.

Table 4 Food diary

Time	*Food eaten or drunk and quantity* (insert letter **b** if you consider this to be a binge)	*Place*	*Compensation used* (i.e. exercise, vomiting)	*Feelings and thoughts*
9 a.m.	Two slices toast, butter, jam	Kitchen at home		Worried, anxious Guilty 'What if I gain weight?' 'I might lose control and not be able to stop'
12.30 p.m.	**b** Three packets of Maltesers Two large bowls of cereal Three packets of crisps Four slices bread with butter and jam One bottle of cola	Bedroom at home	Vomiting	Ashamed, embarrassed, gross 'I am disgusting' 'I am a failure' 'I will never be able to stop this'

Many people find the prospect of writing down everything they have eaten very scary or even pointless. Read the possible stumbling blocks below if you are feeling reluctant to embark on this task and try to think about what your own barriers to completing these diaries might be. Remember that completing this food diary is an essential part of treatment and that you are very unlikely to change without keeping these records.

Possible stumbling blocks

I am scared or ashamed or embarrassed to write down everything I am eating

These are very common emotions for people to describe. However, it is often vital to face up to the reality of your current eating in order to be able to change it. Keeping a food diary can help you do this specifically because it feels difficult. These diaries are only for you; you do not need to show them to anyone else, and therefore it is unlikely that you need to feel ashamed or embarrassed.

I do not see the point in writing down everything I'm eating – it will just make me feel worse

Writing down everything you are eating can often make you feel worse at first. This is again because writing it down means facing up to the reality of what you are doing. Only by writing down what you are doing can you start to understand why your bingeing is happening. It is this very knowledge that is vital in helping you to find ways to change.

I am worried about other people seeing my diary

If you are very worried about this, it may be useful to buy a diary with a lock, or to keep your diary somewhere very safe. This diary is for you only and it is not important that you share it with anyone else unless you want to.

I don't have the time to write this diary

Keeping a food diary in fact takes up very little time. Some people have found it useful to keep a scrap of paper with them at all times and to go to a different room in order to write down what they have just eaten. Remember that while it may feel strange at first, you will very quickly get used to it and it will become an automatic part of your day.

When to move on to the next step

Try to complete a food diary for a full week before you attempt to make any changes to what you are eating. It is very important to fill out this diary *straight after eating* rather than waiting for the evening or the next day. This is because it is actually very difficult to remember exactly what you have eaten, how much you have eaten and how you were feeling if you leave it until the end of the day. When you have managed to complete seven days of the food diary, you will be ready to make initial changes to your eating.

Understanding your eating

When you have completed at least seven days in the diary, the next task is to have a look at the pattern of your eating. With the help of the following chapter, try to think about why you might be bingeing. Ask yourself:

- What tends to be happening when I am bingeing?
- Am I bingeing at a particular time or in a particular place?
- Am I restricting prior to a binge?

Look back at pages 39–40 to help you with this. Once you understand what can trigger your bingeing or why you might be bingeing, you are best placed to change.

Reminder: Have you been completing your quick assessment guide (see page 41)?

8

Changing your eating

The first task in recovering from an eating disorder is to change the pattern of your eating. This may involve changing what you eat, how much you eat or when you eat. Once you are able to maintain a more structured, healthier meal plan, we can then deal with the emotional or psychological part of your eating.

This chapter will take you through examples of healthy eating and appropriate portion sizes, as well as ideas for starting to change your eating. The main task here is to change your eating from long periods of restricting followed by bingeing to a regular, healthy eating pattern. This involves eating *three balanced meals with one to three planned, appropriate snacks* regularly spaced throughout the day. Specific mealtimes can vary depending on your own preferences as well as work and social demands. However, you should try to stick to roughly the same times each day initially and not to leave more than about three or four hours between each meal or snack. The meal plan example given here is provided as a guide to what constitutes healthy eating. Remember that bingeing will not stop without stopping the periods of restriction that occur between bingeing. This may seem very anxiety-provoking or you may feel that you should stop bingeing before you can eat more throughout the day, but remember that bingeing is often triggered by a physiological pressure to eat (even if you don't feel hungry) so you are very unlikely to be able to stop bingeing without increasing or restructuring your eating.

Healthy eating plan

This eating plan is designed for someone of a healthy weight who wants to maintain that weight and to stop bingeing (see Table 5). It should be used as a guide to help you to recognize which foods you need to add into your current meal plan and also as a guide to the structure that your eating should roughly take throughout the day. It may seem overwhelming at first, in which case you may find it easier to plan how you can build up to this meal plan by making changes more gradually, rather than totally changing your eating all at once. Guidance on specific portion sizes is presented in Appendix 1 (pages 105–11). Use this information to help you to develop your own personal, meal plan. Copy Table 6 (page 62) into your diary to record your own daily meal plans. Meal planning should include information about specific foods to be consumed, the amount and the context, for example specific place and time. Planning meals in this way, although it may often feel tedious, overwhelming or scary, is a vital part of overcoming an eating disorder, for the following reasons:

Table 5 Healthy eating plan

Breakfast	1 cup of cereal with 200 ml semi-skimmed milk
	1 slice toast with 1 rounded teaspoon butter or margarine and 1 teaspoon jam
	200 ml fruit juice or 1 piece fruit
	Mug of tea, coffee or other drink
Mid-morning	Mug of tea, coffee or other drink
	A piece of fruit
Lunch	Main meal (can be a cold meal) – must include one portion each of carbohydrates, protein, fat and vegetables or salad
	Light dessert (e.g. yogurt) and a piece of fruit
	400 ml water
Mid-afternoon	Mug of tea, coffee or other drink
	1 snack (e.g. cereal bar)
Dinner	Main meal (includes one portion of carbohydrates, protein, fat and vegetables or salad)
	Light dessert on four days a week, regular dessert on three days a week
	400 ml water or similar drink
Approx. 8 p.m.	Mug of tea, coffee or similar drink and 1 piece fruit (if desired)
Bedtime	Milky drink (200 ml milk with 3–4 teaspoons Horlicks or hot chocolate) or 1 snack (e.g. 2 digestive biscuits)

- It helps ensure you get the full range of nutrients that you need, as you will naturally tend to eat a wider variety of foods.
- Eating according to a predetermined plan helps you to see food as medication intended to decrease the occurrence of extreme food cravings and binge-eating.
- It helps to reduce feelings of guilt and anxiety that are often associated with eating.
- It allows people with eating disorders to relax the often very rigid rules they may have about food and eating.
- It means that you don't have to face very large meals (by spacing out the required calories throughout the day).
- It means that the gaps between meals are likely to be more manageable.
- It helps avoid the feeling that you may lose control of what you are eating.
- People with eating disorders tend to have unreliable or unpredictable internal hunger signals; by planning your meals you are making sure your body receives the nutrients it needs without relying on inaccurate internal sensations.

Meal plan

Table 6 shows how you can plan your meals in advance. Draw out and complete your own version in your notebook; this will make it much easier for you to reintroduce a healthy structure to your eating and help to reduce your anxiety.

Table 6 Meal plan

Meal or snack	*Time*	*Quantity*	*Food and drink*
Breakfast			
Snack			
Lunch			
Snack			
Dinner			
Snack			

Possible stumbling blocks

I am worried that I will gain weight if I change my eating

Think back to what we said about this on page 48. It is very uncommon for people to gain any significant amount of weight when they start to introduce structured eating. The meal plan outlined above is designed to help people of a healthy weight maintain that weight, therefore there is little reason why your weight should increase. Remember that if you are bingeing, even if you are trying to compensate through vomiting or exercise, you will often be consuming more calories than will be contained in your meal plan, so there is no reason you should gain weight when you stop bingeing.

I can't find the time to eat in this way

Often people believe that, because of work or family commitments, they will not be able to find the time to eat in this way. This can be a difficulty sometimes but it is never impossible. It is likely that, in order to overcome your eating disorder, you will have to prioritize the need to eat in this way and do everything you can to make it possible. This may mean talking to people about taking some responsibility from you initially, or planning your day so that you build things around your mealtimes. Remember, though, that eating in this way is never impossible and it is important that you find a way of enabling yourself to do this.

I tried to change my eating but I was still bingeing

One of two things may be happening here. It may be that you are expecting to stop bingeing straight away, and are not giving your body time to adjust to the new meal plan and therefore to stop bingeing. If this is the case, try to maintain your new eating structure for longer, as the likelihood is that you will stop bingeing if you are eating enough throughout the day. Alternatively, it may be that while you think you are sticking to the meal plan you are still finding ways to compensate, for example having very small portions or diet versions of what you are eating, or you may have increased your levels of exercise or other behaviours in order to try to reduce the impact of eating in this way. It is important here to be very honest with yourself: look over your food diary and try to recognize where this may be happening. In order to stop bingeing it is vital that you stick exactly to the meal plan without restricting or compensating at any point.

The emotions associated with eating in this way feel overwhelming

Often people find that when they stop using their eating behaviours, a number of different emotions which they may have tried to block out for a long time through their eating come to the surface. If this happens, look back at Box 1 (pages 49–50) and try to put some of these coping strategies in place to help you to cope with these emotions. It is likely that, as you get used to eating in this way, the emotions will quickly start to reduce. However, it is important that you stick to the meal plan you have devised for long enough to allow this to happen, even though it may feel very difficult. If the emotions you are experiencing feel completely unbearable, it is likely that you may need to seek help from others around you, including medical professionals who will be able to help you to cope with these emotions.

When to move on to the next step

Once you have been able to stick to your meal plan for two weeks, it is fine to move on to the next step, even if you have not yet been able totally to stop bingeing. Remember that stopping bingeing is very difficult and will not happen overnight, but it is important to continue to stick to the meal plan you have devised throughout the next sections of this treatment programme and afterwards.

Reminder: have you been completing your quick assessment guide (see page 41)?

9

Further techniques to help you stop bingeing

In addition to eating in the regular structured way described so far, there are a number of other strategies you can put in place that may help you to reduce the likelihood of bingeing. Below is a list of useful techniques which may help you when you are having urges to binge. These will not work on their own and should always be used in conjunction with restructuring your eating and maintaining a healthy eating plan.

Useful techniques

Avoid high-risk situations

Initially, until your bingeing is under control, it may be a good idea to avoid high-risk situations or events that you know from previous experience are likely to result in you bingeing. If you know that you are likely to binge after seeing certain people or if you have certain food types in your house or in a certain room, it is probably a good idea to avoid putting yourself in these positions while you are trying to stop bingeing. The aim is not to avoid these situations long-term, but rather to reduce the risk of you bingeing until you feel more confident about your ability to resist urges to binge by yourself.

Do one thing at a time

Bingeing often happens when you are distracted by doing something else, for example reading or watching the television. If you are eating food as part of your meal plan, try to do this in a place where you can concentrate on what you are doing rather than while you are on the move or doing something else. If you are bingeing, try to be very aware of what you are doing rather than blocking out or distracting yourself from your eating; this is likely to reduce the size of your binges in the short term.

Delay bingeing

Try delaying bingeing when you have urges to binge. It is very likely that the urges will pass quite quickly – try waiting for 30 minutes, or doing something else and see whether the urge to binge passes during this time. It can be particularly useful to do something that requires concentration or that involves you using your hands, because it will then be more difficult for you to eat (see page 67 for a list of things you could do instead of bingeing).

Remind yourself why you don't want to binge

Here, it can be useful to look back at the reasons you want to stop bingeing that you wrote at the beginning of your therapy notebook. Try to remind yourself of these reasons during times when you are having urges to binge. It can be useful to have a folded piece of paper with your reasons for not bingeing and to keep it on you at all times, or, if possible, to place your list of reasons in a place where you will be likely to see it when you are bingeing, for example on the fridge or cupboard door.

Try not to be too hard on yourself and learn something from slip-ups

Remember that it is very hard to stop bingeing and this rarely happens overnight. It is likely that, especially to begin with, slip-ups will happen. Rather than beating yourself up when this does happen and using them as evidence that you will never stop bingeing, use these experiences to help you resist urges next time. Ask yourself why you binged:

- Had you stuck to your meal plan that day?
- Had you put yourself in a high-risk situation?
- Had something happened just before that had triggered a negative emotion in you?

When you have worked out why you binged, try to think about what you could have done differently and how you might be able to stop yourself from bingeing next time.

Give yourself rewards or praise

Rather than focusing only on the times when you have been unable to resist the urges to binge or purge, think about the times when you have been able to resist or delay bingeing. Perhaps set yourself a goal of not bingeing for a certain amount of time and think about a reward you could give yourself if you meet this goal.

Use alternative behaviours to bingeing and purging

It is important to begin to construct a list of things that you can do rather than bingeing. This will help to distract you from the urges to binge until they pass, reducing the likelihood of you bingeing. The things you write down should be activities you enjoy rather than things that involve chores or working. They should also not be activities that involve being around or dealing with food – don't plan to do an activity in the kitchen or another room in which you usually binge. It might be useful to think about behaviours that you could do outside your house, such as going for a walk, or things that involve your hands, such as painting your nails or washing your hair. Try to come up with a list of a number of different behaviours that you may be able to do at different times. Write this list down in your notebook and try to keep adding to it as you think of more alternative activities.

Initially try out these behaviours when you *do not* have the urge to binge. Later on, try testing them out when you *do* have an urge to binge. If one works, put a star next to it in your notebook and try to remember to repeat this activity whenever you are having urges to binge. Here are some suggestions for alternative behaviours to start you off.

- Go for a walk.
- Call a friend.
- Do your nails.
- Read for half an hour.
- Wash your hair.
- Spent time in a public place.
- Play some music.
- Draw a picture.
- Go to a friend's house.
- Watch a favourite TV programme.

Reminder: have you been completing your quick assessment guide (see page 41)?

10

Challenging your thoughts

On pages 17–18 we talked about the relevance of specific thinking errors in maintaining your eating disorder. Remember that it is your thinking (or the way you interpret events) that influences your feelings. Although this thinking is often difficult to identify, a feeling never exists without a thought (or image) behind it. This chapter takes you through strategies and tasks which can help you to challenge unhelpful ways of thinking and come up with more helpful thinking patterns. Bingeing is often more likely to happen when you feel anxious or low, or are thinking in a negative way about yourself. By identifying the specific thoughts and feelings that may be contributing to a desire to binge, and by challenging these using specific strategies which we will discuss next, you can start to have more control over your eating. Identifying and challenging negative thinking is a skill that, like anything, takes time to get used to and requires practice in order for you to do it well. Each of the techniques listed in this chapter should ideally be used on a daily basis. This will help you to become proficient at challenging

Table 7 Negative thoughts and feelings

Examples of a negative thought	*Examples of feelings or emotions*
• Things will never change	• Anger
• There is no point in trying	• Shame
• I will fail	• Guilt
• I will put on more and more weight	• Fear
• I am useless	• Anxiety
• I can't do this	• Hopelessness
• I shouldn't have eaten that	• Sadness
• No one will ever find me attractive	• Worry
• I am fat	• Disgust

thoughts, and gradually you should feel able to have more control over your negative thinking.

A list of possible negative automatic thoughts and feelings to look out for is given in Table 7 to help you to identify the difference between a thought and a feeling.

Task 1: Self-monitoring

In the same way that recording your eating patterns helped you to identify and understand what was happening with your eating, it is also important to start to understand what is happening with your thoughts. In order to help you do this, we first need to use a thought monitoring record to help you to recognize unhelpful patterns in your thinking. Copy Table 8 overleaf into your therapy notebook, and over the next week try to fill in this table either when you are aware of urges to binge that seem to be driven by an emotional trigger, or simply when you are aware of powerful negative emotions (that may not necessarily be paired with urges to binge). Instructions for filling in this table are given below:

- Copy Table 8 into your therapy diary. The example here is filled in to help you out, but you should fill in the columns for yourself.
- In the Situation column, record where you are and what you are doing or what is happening around you (plus the day and time).
- In the Feelings column, write down what emotions you are experiencing (e.g. angry, upset, guilty). Often you may be feeling a number of emotions, so it is important to write each of them down.
- In the Thoughts column, write down what you were thinking at the time. Try asking yourself, 'Why am I feeling this emotion?' Typically, you will get your thought from asking yourself this question. For example: question, 'Why am I feeling depressed?'; answer, 'I am feeling depressed because I can't do anything right.' In the same way as with feelings, you may have a number of thoughts going through your mind, so record all the ones that are distressing you. If you are struggling to identify any thoughts, however, ask yourself the questions listed in Box 3; these may help you to identify what is going through your mind.

- In the Behaviour column, record what you did as a result of that feeling. This might be that you binged, or it might be some other behaviour such as 'went home early from a party', or 'stayed late at work'.

Table 8 Self-monitoring

Situation	*Thoughts*	*Feelings*	*Behaviour*
At home, just eaten breakfast	'I will get fat' 'I am going to binge' 'I can't get through the day without bingeing'	Guilt Anxiety	Give up and binge
Trying on clothes in a shop	'I am fat' 'I am unattractive' 'Nothing looks good on me'	Sadness Disgust	Do not stick to meal plan
Arguing with boyfriend	'I am unlovable' 'I am in the wrong' 'I am stupid' 'He is going to leave me'	Sadness Anxiety	Binge

It can be very difficult to identify the thoughts that are contributing to your emotions, particularly if you are not used to doing this. Sometimes it may feel as though there are hundreds of thoughts in your head, and sometimes it may feel as though there are none. The important thing to remember is that the more you practise trying to identify your thoughts the easier it will become, so don't give up. Listed in Box 3 are some questions which you may find it useful to ask yourself when you are aware of an intense emotion, in order to help you to work out what the thought might be.

Box 3 Identifying your thoughts

If you are struggling to identify any thoughts the following questions may help:

- What was going through my mind just before I started to feel this way?

- What does this say about me if it is true?
- What does this mean about me, my life, my future?
- What am I afraid might happen?
- What is the worst thing that could happen if it is true?
- What does this mean about how the other person(s) feel(s) or think(s) about me?
- What does this mean about the other person(s) or people in general?
- What images or memories do I have in this situation?

Task 2: Identify thinking errors

Once you have completed these columns, the next task is to try to work out whether the thought is useful or accurate. As we said earlier, people often have thoughts about themselves or about situations which may not be 100 per cent accurate, but which are based on a bias that they have about themselves. In these cases, it can be helpful to try to challenge or evaluate the thoughts that are causing you distress. If you have recorded a number of thoughts, look back at the Thoughts column and choose one thought to challenge. It is very important that you only pick one, as it is almost impossible to evaluate more than one thought at a time. It is normally a good idea to choose the most distressing or upsetting thought to challenge as this is most likely to result in the greatest reduction of your distress. You should also start by challenging a thought that relates to a specific situation, such as 'X thinks what I am saying is stupid' or 'I'm going to put on loads of weight after eating that meal', rather than attempting to challenge a deeper belief that you have about yourself such as 'I am unlovable' or 'I am a failure'. This is because thoughts that relate to specific situations are easier to challenge and therefore are an easier place to start.

In trying to evaluate your thoughts, first review the list of 'cognitive distortions' given below. A cognitive distortion is a way of thinking that can be unhelpful. Remember that we can all be guilty of using cognitive distortions, but that it is important to recognize when these are becoming unhelpful. You may also find it useful to reread the section on thinking errors on pages 17–18 to remind yourself of why these thinking patterns occur. Ask yourself if it is possible that you are using any of the following thinking styles.

NB: If it helps, write down examples of when or how you have used these distortions before.

Cognitive distortions

- All-or-nothing thinking (seeing things in black-and-white categories, e.g. either 'I'm perfect' or 'I'm a failure').
- Overgeneralization (seeing a single negative event as an ongoing pattern of defeat, e.g. 'I didn't do very well in that piece of work so I'll never do well' or 'My last relationship didn't work so I'll never have a successful relationship').
- Mental filter (picking out a single negative event and dwelling on it exclusively, e.g. in your appraisal you only hear the one negative comment made despite receiving lots of positive feedback).
- Disqualifying the positive (rejecting positive experiences by insisting they 'don't count' for some reason or other, e.g. 'My friend only said I looked good because she feels sorry for me').
- Jumping to conclusions (making a negative interpretation even though there are no definite facts, sometimes called mind reading or the fortune teller error, e.g. 'She obviously didn't call me because she hates me' or 'There's no point in arranging to meet up because he'll only cancel on me').
- Magnification (or minimization) (exaggerating the importance of things, such as your own mistake or someone else's achievement, or inappropriately shrinking things until they appear tiny, such as your own desirable qualities or the other person's imperfections).
- Emotional reasoning (assuming that your negative emotions reflect a fact, e.g. 'I feel it, therefore it must be true').
- 'Should' statements (trying to motivate yourself with 'shoulds' and 'shouldn'ts' and often feeling guilty as a result, e.g. 'I should be able to stop bingeing' or 'I shouldn't feel upset that my friend didn't call to see how I was').
- Labelling and mislabelling (attaching a negative label to yourself instead of describing your error, e.g. 'I'm a loser' or 'I'm a failure';

mislabelling involves describing an event with language that is highly coloured and emotionally loaded).

- Personalization (seeing yourself as the cause of some negative external event which in fact you are not primarily responsible for, e.g. 'It must be my fault that my colleague was upset in work today').

If you think that you may be using one or more of these cognitive distortions, write down in your therapy diary which distortions you are using. Try to think about what thought you might have if you were *not* using this cognitive distortion.

Task 3: Learning to challenge the thought

In learning to challenge thoughts, it is important to try to evaluate each thought – to ask yourself whether it is 100 per cent certain that this thought is true and that there is no other way of looking at this situation. It is very likely that you will 'feel' that this thought is true, but even though this can be very powerful it is a subjective view, not a reliable piece of evidence. Try to evaluate objectively whether it is a 'fact' that this thought is true. Imagine that you are in front of a jury and are trying to convince them that the thought you are having is 100 per cent accurate. Would the evidence you provide to support the thought hold up in court? Remember that a fact is very different from a feeling. In your therapy diary, draw up two columns and mark them 'For' and 'Against'. Write down as much evidence as you can think of that the thought may be either true or not true, and remember this evidence should be factual: that is, if you asked someone else he or she would agree that it is definitely evidence that the thought is true or not true, rather than being another assumption or negative thought. It can be helpful to ask other people at this point, or to ask yourself what you would say of other people. Table 9 overleaf gives examples of this for the negative thought 'I'm no good at anything'.

Table 9 'I'm no good at anything': for and against

Evidence for thought (What is the evidence to suggest that this thought is true?)	*Evidence against thought (What is the evidence to suggest that this thought is not true?)*
• I binged this morning	• I have friends who care about me
• I had an argument with my partner yesterday	• Everyone argues sometimes, it doesn't mean it's my fault
• My boss doesn't like me	• I don't know that my boss doesn't like me, she is not very nice to most people at work
• The report I did yesterday got returned to me	• Usually I get good feedback at work
	• I got promoted last year so I can't be terrible at my job

After both columns have been completed, look at the For column again and ask yourself for each piece of evidence: 'Is this really true?' or 'How reliable is this piece of evidence?' If you can think of any reasons why the 'evidence for' might not be true, add these to the Against column.

In addition, the following questions may help you to evaluate the thought you have written down:

- Would this be true for another person? (Often we have very different standards for ourselves from those we have for others, so where we might see ourselves negatively following a particular situation, we would not see others negatively if they were in the same situation. An example of this might be failing a driving test or a relationship ending. We might see these as evidence that we are a failure or unlovable, but we would not apply these same rules to others. Recognizing when we might be judging ourselves too harshly or critically is an important step in trying to be more compassionate towards ourselves.)
- What is the factual evidence for this thought being true? (Often people take thoughts or feelings to be fact without stopping to think about whether they really are. Make sure, in your For column, that everything you have written down is a fact, not just another negative thought or assumption.)

- How do I *know* this thought is true? (Would you be able to defend this thought in court or is it just how you *feel*?)
- Is there anything to suggest that this thought might not be true? (Are you able to find *any* evidence, no matter how small, that contradicts this thought or suggests that it might not be true?)
- What would someone else say about this thought? (If you asked a close friend or family member, would they agree that this thought is accurate?)
- Would I judge other people by these standards? (Would I say the same about my sister, daughter, best friend, if she presented the same evidence to me?)
- Are these thoughts helping me to get on with people that I care about? (Do I really want to keep these thoughts? Are they helpful to me or might it be better to try to let them go?)
- Are there any consequences of thinking like this that I might not want? (If you continue to think like this, what will be the outcome? How will you feel? Is this something you want?)
- Do I hold the same set of rules for others? (If someone else said that he or she was worried about this happening or told me he or she was thinking in the same way, what would I say in reply? If my best friend or someone I loved had this thought, what would I tell him or her?)
- Is there *any* other way of looking at this event?
- Is this problem as bad or as significant as I am making it out to be?
- How likely is it that the worst thing or feared consequence will happen?
- Are there any advantages in adopting a different viewpoint or selecting an alternative thought?
- Have I had any experiences that show that this (thought) is not completely true all the time?
- If my best friend or someone who loves me knew I was thinking this thought, what would that person say to me? (What evidence would my friend point out to me that would suggest that my thoughts were not 100 per cent true?)
- When I am not feeling this way, do I think about this type of situation any differently? How?

- When I have felt this way in the past, what did I think about that helped me to feel better?
- Have I been in this type of situation before? What happened? Is there anything different between this situation and previous ones? What have I learned from prior experiences that could help me now?
- Are there any small things that contradict my thoughts that I might be discounting as not important?
- Five years from now, if I look back at this situation, will I look at it any differently? Will I focus on any different part of my experience?
- Are there any strengths or positives in me or the situation that I am ignoring?
- Am I jumping to conclusions that are not completely justified by the evidence?
- Am I blaming myself for something over which I do not have complete control?
- Look back over the list of thinking errors on pages 72–3. Are you using any of these unhelpful ways of thinking? If so, ask yourself: if I wasn't using this distortion, what might I think?

Another important question to ask yourself in trying to challenge the original thought is 'Is this a helpful way of thinking?' To help you do this, in your therapy diary draw up two columns, headed Advantages and Disadvantages as in Table 10, and generate the advantages of thinking this way and the disadvantages of thinking this way.

Table 10 Is this a helpful way of thinking?

Advantages *(What are the advantages of thinking this way?)*	*Disadvantages* *(What are the disadvantages of thinking this way?)*
• I have lower expectations of myself so might not feel as bad if I do badly	• I feel bad anyway • If I tell myself I'm no good, I usually end up doing worse at things • When I tell myself I'm bad, I tend not to notice anything that I do well

After both columns have been completed, look at the Advantages column again, and for each point you have made ask yourself: 'Is this really an advantage?' If you think of anything that is not in fact helpful or advantageous, write it down next to the original point.

By now, you should hopefully begin to see that it is possible that the original thought you were having may be your interpretation of the situation rather than a fact: that is, it is a subjective view rather than a truth. If you are starting to realize that the way you are feeling may be a result of an unhelpful thought you are having, try to provide yourself with an alternative thought (see below) to help you to change or reduce the intensity of the emotions you are experiencing.

Task 4: Finding an alternative thought

The final task in challenging your thinking is to develop an alternative thought. Look back at the original thought that you decided to challenge and then look at all the information you have generated in the tables and questions above. Put this all together to generate an alternative thought. The alternative thought does not have to be completely different: it can be a slightly nicer or less rigid thought than the original thought you were having. An example is given in Table 11 overleaf. Write down your alternative thought in your therapy notebook and underline it. Rate how much you believe the alternative thought. It is really important that you believe it 100 per cent. If you don't believe your alternative thought 100 per cent, delete the part of your response that is preventing you from believing it completely, or change the response slightly so that you can believe it completely. Once you have generated an alternative thought, it is often helpful to try to remind yourself of this thought on a regular basis, or to write it out and place it somewhere where you are likely to look at it frequently. Some people find it useful to write out their alternative thought on a small piece of paper and keep it in their wallet or somewhere close by. This is certainly a good idea for the thoughts that keep coming into your mind, as you will then be able to read your alternative thought when you have the original thought and are feeling distressed.

Finally, when you have come up with an alternative thought that you believe, ask yourself if there is anything else you can do other than what you have written in the Behaviour column of your chart (see page 70). It is likely that your initial behavioural response may have been unhelpful or unhealthy, so ask yourself if there is anything else you could do to cope with or manage the emotions you are left with.

Table 11 Alternative thoughts

Original thought	*Example of alternative thought*
I'm no good at anything	Everyone makes mistakes sometimes, me included, and this doesn't mean I can't do anything right. In fact, sometimes I have done things all right in the past

Possible stumbling blocks

I can't identify a thought to challenge

Sometimes it can be difficult to identify exactly what we are thinking, but every emotion will stem from a thought. Identifying thoughts is a skill and therefore can take some time to get right. Keep going through the list of prompts listed in Box 3 (pages 70–1) and write down any thought you think might be contributing to the emotion, even if you are not certain. If you really can't identify any thought, don't give up; perhaps try again in another situation when you may find it easier to work out what you are thinking.

I can't challenge the thought

Again, challenging negative thoughts can be very difficult. We are motivated to hang on to our initial thoughts as they are often the easiest thoughts, and because we may have held them as true for so long challenging them can feel uncomfortable. This is something you will get better at the more you try. Perhaps try first with the thought you have rated yourself as having the lowest belief in: ask someone you trust to help you challenge the thought or try challenging at a time when your emotions are less intense. This way, it may become easier to challenge thoughts when they are stronger.

I can't find any evidence against the initial thought

If you really can't find any evidence, try asking someone else, or ask yourself what evidence you would look for if you were helping someone else to challenge that thought. Alternatively, try first defining the adjective you have used in the initial thought and comparing yourself to that definition. For example, if your initial thought is 'I am useless', ask yourself how a dictionary might define 'useless' and whether you fit this criterion exactly. Is there any way that you wouldn't exactly fit the dictionary definition of 'useless'?

I don't really believe the alternative thought

It is very important that you believe the alternative thought 100 per cent. If you don't, try compromising between the initial thought and the alternative thought to enable you to believe the alternative thought; for example, instead of 'I am . . .' try, 'I might not be . . .' or 'Sometimes I am . . .' Remember that the alternative thought doesn't have to be the complete opposite of the initial thought.

I still feel the same after I've challenged the thought

Challenging thoughts, like any skill, takes time to get right. Remember that we are not aiming to eradicate the initial emotions but to reduce their intensity, even a little bit. As you get used to challenging thoughts, it is probable that your emotions will start to shift but this may not happen straight away. Emotions are difficult to change, but the important thing is that you keep trying and do not give up just because you don't feel better straight away.

Trying to find evidence for and against a thought you believe to be true, and coming up with an alternative thought, is *always* difficult at first. Remember that the negative thoughts we have about ourselves can be very strong and we do not easily feel able to give them up. There are a number of things you can do to make this process work better, including:

- Make sure you pick *one* automatic thought to evaluate.
- Make sure everything you have listed in the Evidence column is a *fact*, not an assumption or opinion, or a separate negative automatic thought.

- Ask yourself 'Does the "evidence for" provide 100 per cent accurate evidence that the automatic thought is true?'
- Make sure that your alternative thought relates directly to the automatic thought and is not just a separate thought.
- Make sure that you are able to believe the alternative thought, otherwise it will have little impact. If you don't, you may need to change it until you are able to find a new thought that you can believe.
- Finally, it is important that you repeat the alternative thought to yourself regularly for it to have full impact. It won't work after just one time as it is trying to fight a thought that you have repeated to yourself over and over again.

When to move on to the next step

There is again no right answer as to when you should move on to the next step. We would, however, encourage you to feel confident and familiar with the challenging techniques before embarking on further tasks. Remember that the challenging skills are life-long ones: that is, they are skills you should continue to use frequently until such time as they become automatic and you no longer hold the initial belief. It makes sense that, if you have held an unhelpful belief for years, it will not change overnight; rather, it may take months or even years to fully engage in and believe your more helpful way of thinking.

Reminder: have you been completing your quick assessment guide (see page 41)?

11
Problem-solving

In addition to regulating your eating and learning to challenge your thinking, learning to problem-solve can also be a very important part of overcoming an eating disorder. Sometimes, no matter how much you challenge your thinking or try to reduce the physiological urges to binge, the emotional need to binge can be a result of a something that you cannot change by thinking differently. In these circumstances it is important to think about how you might be able to change (or problem-solve) the situation you are in. Effective problem-solving can help you when you encounter difficulties in your recovery, as well as when you have difficulties in other areas of your life which may be having an impact on your eating. As we explained in Chapter 3 of this book, eating disorders can often be linked to difficulties at work, in relationships or in other important areas of your life. This chapter will show you a set of skills intended to help you learn effective strategies to overcome some of these difficulties.

Define the problem

Problems are things you are able to change, obstacles you might want or need to overcome or challenges you need to meet. Problems are very different from facts. Think hard about whether your situation is a problem – that is, something that can be changed – or a fact – something over which you have no control. If what you are facing is a fact, you will need to think about how you can deal with or learn to cope with this fact, rather than how you can change or overcome it. Examples of facts would be splitting up with a partner, losing somebody close to you, not getting a promotion last year, not getting the grades you were predicted in your exams. Examples of problems would be not being able to talk openly to your partner, not managing your time well at work, not having planned anything to do at the weekend, not seeing your friends enough.

The first step in effective problem-solving is knowing exactly what the problem is and what you want to be different. In order to help you to define a specific problem, try asking yourself the following questions:

- What emotion am I feeling, and what events or situations are contributing to this emotion?
- What *exactly* am I not happy about at the moment? (Try to be as specific as possible.)
- How does this affect me?
- How does this affect other people around me?
- Can I do anything to change any aspect of the events or situations I've identified as problematic?
- Does this situation need to be changed?
- Is there any good in this situation?

To help you work out how this might relate to your eating disorder, go back to your eating diary. Are there specific situations in which you are more likely to binge? For example, some people report bingeing after seeing a particular friend or group of friends, after or before particular meetings at work or when they are in a particular place.

If you find you are confronted with a number of different interrelated problems, prioritize which problem you want to deal with first (this can be either the easiest problem to overcome or the one you see as the most important).

Try to think about why the problem might be happening. What is getting in the way of or stopping something happening, or perhaps, what are you or someone else doing that might be causing the problem?

Make sure you know exactly what you want to be different: that is, define your outcome. Be realistic – outcomes must be attainable, observable and measurable. It is also important to consider the worst-case scenario. This is real life and things do not always work out as we would like. Ask yourself: what would be the worst thing that would happen? How bad would this really be, and how would I deal with it if it happened?

Try to find alternative solutions to the problem

Once you have defined both the problem and the outcome you hope for in overcoming or changing it, try to write down as many possible solutions as you can think of to this problem. Write things down even if they seem impossible or unrealistic. It can be useful to ask yourself :

- What advice would I give to X if he or she had this difficulty?
- What do I think X would do if he or she was in this situation?
- What have I done in any similar situations before?

Alternatively, if you feel able, ask other people you trust or respect what they might do or have done in a similar situation.

Try to come up with as extensive a list as you can and make sure you have all of your ideas written down in the same place.

Select one of these solutions to try out

When you have written down as many possible solutions as you can think of, the next task is to select one of these solutions to test out. In making the decision about which solution to test out first, ask yourself :

1. Which possible solution is most likely to solve the problem in the long term?
2. What are the pros and cons of each of these possible solutions?
3. Which approach is the most realistic to accomplish for now?
4. What is the extent of risk associated with each alternative?

Remember, there is not always a simple or perfect solution to every difficulty. Ask yourself whether it is worth trying to change the problem even if the solution is not perfect. Is a small change better than no change at all? What will happen if you don't try to change or overcome the situation?

Implement this solution

Once you have selected which one of your possible solutions you want to try to implement first, think about how exactly you are going to do this. Ask yourself what you will need to do in order to implement this solution, when you are going to do this, whether you need to talk to anyone else about it first . . .

Evaluate whether this solution has solved the problem

If you do not feel that it has solved the problem, go back to your list and try out one of the other possible solutions that you have written down. Keep doing this until you have found a solution that works.

Reminder: have you been completing your quick assessment guide (see page 41)?

12

Body image

Disturbance or extreme dissatisfaction with your own body image and increased preoccupation with appearance are core features of an eating disorder. It is rare for people with an eating disorder not to say that they focus very heavily and place a lot of importance on their body shape and weight. Body image dissatisfaction is usually the reason people start dieting in the first place, and research suggests that changes in eating patterns are largely predicted by changes in body satisfaction. Dissatisfaction with body image is often reported as the main trigger to relapse of an eating disorder, and as such it is important to pay significant attention to your body image and to use strategies to try to improve your feelings towards your body. Often, people with an eating disorder derive most of their self-esteem from how satisfied they feel with their body. In comparison, people without eating disorders will be more likely to derive their self-esteem from a number of different domains – for example, quality of relationships, achievements at work, enjoyment of socializing, quality of friendships or family relationships, feedback from colleagues or friends, compliments given by others, previous successes, etc. – with appearance or body satisfaction usually contributing only a small amount to a person's overall self-esteem.

Look back at the two pie charts in Figure 4 (page 25) to compare the elements that make up the self-esteem of someone who has an eating disorder compared to someone who does not. Unfortunately, people with an eating disorder tend to have very low satisfaction with their body, no matter what their shape or size. This means that most people with an eating disorder will have a lower self-esteem; as we said before, it's like having all your eggs in one basket. The aim of addressing your body image dissatisfaction in this chapter is not that you will feel 100 per cent satisfied with everything about your body – after all, very few, especially women, would say that of themselves. Rather, you should feel able to accept your body and not let your body image disproportionately affect how you feel about yourself as a person or how you live your life.

What is body image?

Body image is not just about your shape or size; it is made up of the thoughts and feelings you have about your body, your subjective perception of your body and the way you behave in response to all of these. Body image is never a fact: it is a subjective opinion, and therefore, while you may not always be able to change your body shape, you *can* change your body image.

Your body image can fluctuate dramatically, even within the same day. Think about the last week: has how you've thought and felt about your body varied? If so, it is unlikely that your body shape has changed in any significant way, so it is your body image that has changed. Many things, apart from your actual shape and weight, can affect your body image. Below, we have listed a number of things that may result in a change in your body image. Have a think about when, over the last week, your body image has been worse and what might have been influencing this change.

- overestimation of size (perception)
- negative mood
- consumption of feared foods
- viewing media images of thin women
- pre-menstruation
- negative emotional state (e.g. loneliness)
- focusing on one (disliked) part of your body
- body 'checking' (an explanation of this is given below)
- avoiding things as a result of your body image
- comparing yourself with others
- wearing certain clothes
- comments from others (either misinterpreted comments or comments that could be perceived as bullying).

Body perception: what is normal?

Body mass index, or BMI, is a way of comparing one person's weight with another's. Obviously, the relevance of being a 14-stone male athlete is different from being a 14-stone female office worker. Further, someone at 10 stone might be overweight if he or she is short or underweight if very tall. Body mass index in effect 'neutralizes' the effect of height and the figures can equally apply to both sexes. Though it does not actually measure the percentage of body fat, it is used to estimate a healthy body weight based on a person's height. Thanks to its ease of measurement and calculation, it is usually the most widely used diagnostic tool to identify weight problems, whether individuals are underweight, overweight or obese. The calculation is made by dividing body weight in kilograms by the square of the height in metres (there are many websites that will do this calculation for you, such as <www.nhs.uk/Tools/Pages/Healthyweightcalculator.aspx>). Thus, a person who is 1.63 m tall and weighs 53.2 kg has a BMI of 20. The 'normal' range of BMI is 20–25; 25–30 is 'overweight', and over 30 is 'obese'. Weights below 20 are 'underweight' and below 17.5 indicative of anorexia.

It is very unusual for people to say that they feel completely satisfied with their body; however, the extent to which we let our body image influence our feelings, our sense of worth and the way we live our lives can vary immensely. Below are some figures that relate to what is 'normal'. Have a think about how you compare to these figures and whether you may be judging your body too harshly.

'Normal'

- A healthy BMI range is 20–25.
- The average BMI for women is about 25.
- Under 10 per cent of women in the UK are underweight (that is, have a BMI of less than 20).
- Over half of women in the UK are overweight (have a BMI of over 25).
- The average clothing size for females in the UK is a size 16.
- It is estimated that 80 per cent of women feel dissatisfied with their body and 90 per cent of women would change something about their appearance.
- Only 2 per cent of women would say that they feel beautiful.

For a table of average weights and heights, see Appendix 2 (page 112).

Ideas for improving body image

Below are a number of things that people often do that may result in them having a poorer body image. Suggestions are given for how to change or cope with each of these.

Do you 'think' about your body in a negative way?

You may already have started to record lots of negative thoughts you have about your body in the thought-monitoring diary you started in Chapter 10. It is not uncommon for people to have negative thoughts about their body. However, these are not helpful and can be challenged in the same was as negative thoughts we have about ourselves or other people.

What can I do about this?

Over the next week, in your therapy notebook keep a diary of situations that provoke both positive or negative thoughts about your appearance. When you are aware of your body image being worse, try to identify the specific thoughts that you are having about your body.

Using the skills you have already learned, try to challenge these thoughts by asking yourself:

- How true is this thought?
- Is there any evidence that this thought is true?
- Is the evidence I'm using to support this thought reliable or subjective?
- Is there any evidence to suggest that this thought might not be true?
- Would I talk to a friend in the way that I am talking to myself?
- What might a friend say to me if I shared this thought with him or her?

Try to come up with an alternative thought that you feel happy with. Remember that this does not have to be a positive thought about your body, but can be a neutral thought. An example of common thoughts, along with more helpful alternative thoughts, is given in Table 12.

Table 12 Helpful alternative thoughts

Initial thought	*Alternative thought*
I am fat	I do not always feel good about my body but some people have suggested otherwise
I am ugly	Attractiveness is subjective; not everyone will see me in the way I see myself
No one will ever find me attractive	Some people have found me attractive in the past

Do you find yourself saying 'But I *feel* fat?'

People with eating disorders often talk about 'feeling fat'. However, fat is a physical description: it is very different from an emotion which you 'feel'. Technically, you cannot 'feel' fat, any more than you can 'feel' square or you can 'feel' that your eyes are blue.

What can I do?

The language we use to talk about our bodies is important. Since it is not possible to 'feel' fat, it is probably more accurate to say 'I think I am fat.' In this case, go back to the challenging negative body image thoughts section (pages 88–9) and try to use a more neutral language to describe yourself. This is very difficult to do at first, but with practice it will become easier.

Alternatively, it may be that you are actually experiencing a different emotion related to an event or situation, such as anger, sadness or anxiety. Feeling fat can often be a smokescreen to how you are really feeling. For example, when people are stressed at work or have had an argument with someone they care about, they may focus on their body image and feel more dissatisfied with their appearance. Ask yourself *why* you are 'feeling fat' in that moment. If you are able to identify any other emotion that you might be experiencing, try to focus on this emotion rather than on your body, and think about how you can cope with it. Think back to the strategies for coping with emotions on pages 81–2 to help you with this.

Another possibility is that you may be experiencing a physical sensation such as fullness, being bloated or feeling hot. Have a think about whether you can replace the word 'fat' in the statement 'I feel fat' with any other words: for example, 'I feel bloated . . . full . . . uncomfortable . . . hot.' If you can, remind yourself that these physical sensations are only temporary, may be very normal and generally do not mean that you are fat.

Do you avoid doing or wearing certain things because of your body?

People with poor body image often avoid certain situations which trigger anxiety or distress. This avoidance maintains the body image disturbance because you start to feel that you *can't* do these things because of your body and as a result feel worse about your body. As such, avoidance of any situation due to body image concerns only serves to maintain anxiety and distress about body image.

What can I do?

Try to identify what you are avoiding because of your body image. For example, commonly avoided actions include avoiding public places or social situations, looking in mirrors, nudity, certain types of clothing or physical activities such as swimming or hugging. In order to reduce distress associated with body image, it may be important to start to 'expose' yourself to each of the things you avoid. This is likely to increase anxiety or distress in the short term; however, this short-term anxiety shouldn't last. We know that the more you do things, the less anxious you start to feel when doing them.

Exposure to these feared or avoided situations should be approached in a graded way: try to challenge yourself by exposure to the least anxiety-provoking situation first and work your way up through the list of avoided situations. You should also try to keep experiencing the feared situation regularly until you feel relaxed about it. Challenging yourself just once is very unlikely to be enough.

Remember that the first time you do this, it is likely to be difficult and anxiety-provoking – in fact, this feeling may continue for the first few times – but the more you do it the easier it will get.

While challenging yourself is difficult, it is a very important part of making changes. Being able to do what you may previously have avoided means that your body image starts to have less of an influence over your life, and therefore your emotions.

Do you 'check' certain parts of your body or focus on certain parts you don't like?

People with eating disorders often report 'checking' certain parts of their body. This usually involves repeated efforts to inspect, measure or correct some aspect of their appearance. Common examples of body checking include frequent weighing, repeatedly looking in the mirror, trying on numerous outfits before leaving the house, adjusting clothes to hide certain body parts, feeling or pinching parts of your body or measuring the size of a particular body part. These behaviours only serve to maintain body dissatisfaction and anxiety, since you continue to focus on those aspects of your body that you do not like.

What can I do?

It is important to try to reduce the frequency of these checking behaviours. This can feel difficult at first because it is likely to increase your anxiety in the short term. However, as with the avoided behaviours, this anxiety will not continue and will reduce in the long term, leaving you with lower body-related anxiety. Often these behaviours will have been done so often that you may feel they have become unconscious or automatic. As with changing any habit, it will take time and effort to stop. You should immediately stop these behaviours every time you become aware of yourself doing them, and gradually they will become less automatic. Often when people are unhappy with a particular part of their body they will focus on that area when looking in the mirror. Try looking at yourself as a whole, acknowledging any bits you are happier with rather than focusing only on the areas you are unsatisfied with.

Do you compare yourself to others and usually feel worse about yourself when you do this?

People with an eating disorder often spend significant amounts of time comparing themselves to others. This often triggers negative thoughts relating to body image and self-worth. Social comparison is something that most of us do. However, who we chose to compare ourselves with and on what dimensions can vary greatly. If you are aware of generally feeling worse after comparing yourself to others, this will almost certainly be maintaining your poor body image.

What can I do?

It is important to try to reduce or change the amount or way in which you compare yourself to others. Remember that research shows it is very difficult to accurately perceive either your own or other people's size and, as such, comparisons are unlikely to be accurate. Comparisons are generally unhelpful as they are usually not made against a broad range of people but rather against a narrow group of people. People with eating disorders tend only to compare themselves with people who they see as very slim or attractive.

Have a think about who you are choosing to compare yourself with – is this helpful to you and does that person accurately represent the normal population? Next time you notice you are comparing yourself to someone, try to look at everyone else in the room or the street as well, in order to get a more representative view. Alternatively, think about other dimensions on which you could compare yourself to others, such as your personality, your job, your friendship groups or your interests. It is important to try to see people as a whole rather than making a judgement based solely on appearance, and therefore not to make comparisons which are likely to make you feel worse about yourself.

It may also be helpful to practise replacing negative statements with more neutral ones: for example, replacing the comparative 'She is much thinner than I am' with the less self-critical 'She has a lovely figure.'

Do you read magazines and compare yourself to magazine images?

Studies show that women's magazines emphasize thinness and dieting, and that increased exposure to this pressure is linked to body shape dissatisfaction and vulnerability to eating disorders.

In modern Western societies, there is now intense pressure on women to be thin. In recent decades, the role models for physical attractiveness that women have been confronted with by the entertainment and fashion industries have become increasingly thin, so that they are representative of very few women in the actual population. It is worth repeating that, over the previous 20 years, the 'ideal' body shape portrayed in the media has become more similar to that of a prepubescent, immature girl's body. Interestingly, this is the exact opposite to the changes in women's body shapes occurring in the general population, where body height and weight have become larger. Thus, the images that women are faced with in the media are become increasingly unrealistic and unrepresentative of the 'normal' population.

As the 'ideal' body shape has become thinner, there is increased pressure to follow weight-loss diets, and a corresponding increase in eating-related problems such as anorexia nervosa and bulimia nervosa. There are high levels of eating disorders among women working in modelling and the fashion industry. As we have already seen, for most women, achieving this body shape would require losing so much body fat that it would become impossible to maintain normal menstrual functioning, normal libido (interest in sexual activity) and normal levels of reproductive hormones. Although extreme dieting has many harmful effects, both physically and psychologically, in general the health benefits of thinness have been overemphasized in the media and the harmful effects of dieting have been overlooked.

What can I do?

All women living in modern Western society are subjected to high levels of these sociocultural pressures. Some women realize that reading certain magazines is distressing because the images are all of impossibly thin models, and choose not to read them, but it is almost impossible to totally control your exposure to these pressures. However, it is more possible to control your reaction to these messages. Thinking about the following can help when you are confronted with these images:

- *Thin media*: images in the media do not represent the great range of body shapes in the world and unfortunately often only depict very thin women rather that celebrating the variety that exists. This means we are left with a very narrow, unrepresentative and unrealistic view of what is attractive.

- *Artificial beauty*: not only are the models we see in the media unrealistically thin and attractive, but these images are often drastically altered by airbrushing to produce an even more 'perfect' image. The prolific use of airbrushing means what we see in the media is not reality.
- *Genetic reality*: everyone is born with a predisposition to look a certain way. For most of us, our genes mean it is impossible to be as thin as models we see in the media. There are three billion women in the world who don't look like supermodels, and only eight women who do.

Other things to try

Engage in pleasurable bodily experiences

Try to increase the number of pleasurable experiences you give your body. This will help you not only to appreciate your body, but also to increase the number of positive experiences associated with the body. Examples of this are having a relaxing bath, treating your body to a massage or spending some time pampering yourself.

Remind yourself of what's *good* about your body

It is very easy to think about your body only in terms of its attractiveness. However, spend some time thinking about what your body is for, what it allows you to do and what you would be unable to do without it. Without your body you would be unable to do day-to-day things like talking to friends, walking around or giving someone a hug. Your body is amazing, and it is unlikely that it deserves the hard time you give it. Spend time thinking about the things you are grateful to your body for, and all the things it is useful for other than just to provide you with an appearance.

Possible stumbling blocks

I don't want to accept my body, I want it to be different

This is a common stumbling block as most people who binge-eat want to change the way they look. It is not possible to stop bingeing if you are trying to lose weight. Recovering from an eating disorder means in the short term accepting your body as it is. It is possible that in the future you might want to focus on changing your body, and in some cases this may be possible. However, remember everything discussed in this chapter and think about how realistic or helpful this will be for you.

I still feel the same about my body

We know that body image can be the slowest part of an eating disorder to change, so don't worry if you feel nothing is changing. It can take months to learn to accept your body. Think about how long you have felt unhappy with your body: it may not be realistic to expect this to change quickly. Even small improvements in your body image can have a great impact on your life.

When to stop recording and meal planning

It is worth considering that many of the skills described in this book are life-long skills: that is, they should become automatic and as such used throughout life. However, you may want to stop other skills, such as using your food diary daily,. It is likely that you will know when you feel ready to stop using your food diary, but remember that this is a tool that can be useful in helping you to stop bingeing. As such, your food diary should be a tool you use until you feel that your bingeing has stopped and your eating has become regular.

Reminder: have you been completing your quick assessment guide (see page 41)?

13

Relapse prevention

What is relapse prevention?

The idea behind relapse prevention is to help you to plan for and cope with possible triggers or events that may result in a relapse in the future. When people have had an eating disorder, it has often been the easiest and sometimes the most successful way of coping with difficult emotions and situations in the past. Even though you may feel as though you have a number of alternative ways of coping now, it is possible that at some point in the future you may feel tempted to revert to your old eating disorder behaviours. By planning for situations that may increase the likelihood of you relapsing and constructing a plan for what to do if you feel yourself slipping back to old behaviours, you can help prevent a full relapse.

What is a slip, lapse or relapse?

In relapse prevention we talk about slips, lapses and relapses. These things are all very different and you should act differently according to what is happening.

- A slip might be something like cutting out lunch or dinner in response to a difficult situation or feeling anxious. These are likely to be quite common, especially at first, but as long as you recognize that this is happening before it leads to bingeing or other behaviours, you will be able to prevent it from turning into anything more than a slip.
- A lapse might be not sticking to your meal plan for a day or two in response to a negative event.
- A relapse might be a prolonged period of restriction and bingeing that you feel unable or unwilling to get out of.

Each of these situations should be dealt with in a different way. The following are some suggestions for ways to prepare for lapses and prevent relapses. If a relapse does occur, however, this does not mean that you will be unable to recover or that any future recoveries will also result in a relapse.

Activity 1: Preparing a lapse plan

A lapse plan is a plan that you should put into place if you feel that you have had a minor setback in your recovery. Think about all the things that have helped you to get to where you are now, as well as all the things you would want to remember to do or to think about should a lapse occur. Write down a list of as many things that you can think of in your therapy notebook, so that you will know where to find these things and be able to put them in place. An example of a lapse plan is given in Box 4.

Box 4 My lapse plan

Triggers or risk factors which may increase my chances of relapse: I may need to look out for warning signs or put some aspects of my lapse plan in place if or when these events occur:

- relationship difficulties
- pressure or increasing demands at work
- life events (marriage, moving house)
- unhealthy comparisons with others re weight or eating.

Warning signs to look out for that suggest I may need to put my lapse plan in place:

- any changes to my eating, for example cutting out foods, delaying eating during the day, not eating in the evening
- urges to binge, buying more binge foods
- use of any compensatory behaviours (vomiting, laxative use, exercise, etc.)
- a drop in my mood
- chronic increasing anxiety
- increasing my focus on shape and weight
- increase in weight- or body-checking behaviours
- increasing preoccupation with food
- increasing dissatisfaction with body image
- decreasing motivation to stay well.

The things I will need to put in place if any of the warning signs occur:

- Identify the triggers or life events relevant to the lapse.
- Try to tackle any life problems head on (use problem-solving techniques rather than retreating into thoughts about food).
- Restart the food diary and take care to avoid log gaps in eating or restriction of any sort.
- Ensure eating is regular, flexible and varied.

Try to identify risks to bingeing and avoid putting myself at unnecessary risk (e.g. eat with X, avoid buying X).

- Talk to X.
- Ensure that I continue to see friends, socialize and engage in the activities I enjoy whenever possible.
- Read through my therapy notebook to remind myself of what has helped before.
- Reread motivations and remind myself of the reasons I don't want my eating disorder.
- Reread the letter I wrote to myself when I first recovered from my eating disorder.

Remember, minor lapses are normal and part of the process of recovery. Try not to be over-critical of yourself if and when they happen, and don't use this as an excuse to give up. React positively and put your lapse plan in place to help you get back on track as soon as possible.

If the lapse continues for more than three or four weeks, it may be worth seeking further help: for example, go to see your GP or seek support and advice from an eating disorders support line (numbers given on page 118).

Activity 2: Preparing for possible triggers to relapse

By now, you probably have a good idea of the triggers to your bingeing as well as the things that contributed to the start of your eating disorder. It can be very useful to think about, and prepare for, any events that might trigger a relapse in the future. This way you can be prepared for these events and will know how to respond to them, so that it will be less likely that these triggers will result in a relapse.

Activity 3: Writing a letter to yourself

Chose a moment when you are feeling strong and grateful to be free of your eating disorder, and use this time to write a letter to yourself about the process of your recovery, how you feel about your eating disorder, how you feel about the changes you have made and the reasons you would like to maintain these changes. Try to make this letter as positive and informative as possible, so that if you read it back to yourself at a much later date you will be able to remember exactly how you felt when you wrote it. Again, write this letter either in your therapy notebook or in a place where you will easily be able to find it should you need to read it later on. Try to keep the letter for times when you are struggling to sustain changes or when your motivation to maintain your recovery is wavering – read over it during these times to help you think openly about which way you want to go.

Activity 4: Preparing a crisis plan

Obviously, sometimes relapses do happen and it can often be difficult to maintain recovery, especially during more stressful or difficult times. If this should happen and you feel you have done all you can, devise a crisis plan with contact numbers and details of people you can talk to who may be able to offer you the support you need to get back on track. In 'Useful addresses' (page 118) we have included details of some possible sources of support; however, you may have other ideas about what you want to do if you feel that things are getting on top of you or you feel unable to deal with any difficulties yourself.

Reminder: have you been completing your quick assessment guide (see page 41)?

14

Further help and treatment: what to do if this hasn't been enough

In the 'Useful addresses' section (page 118) we have listed a number of sources of further support which may be useful to you. This chapter gives further information about treatment options.

What other options for treatment are there?

Eating difficulties can be very difficult to change. If you have worked through this treatment programme and feel that you are still suffering with your eating difficulties, it is likely that you may need help from someone else.

If this is the case, there are a range of treatment options for you. Effective treatments have been developed from years of research and clinical experience; many people recover fully from their eating disorder after seeking help. Despite this, we know that many people do not seek help for their binge-eating. Why not?

They aren't ready to change

Some people do not seek help because they are not ready to change. Recovery from an eating disorder can seem daunting, and committing yourself to change can be a scary and difficult thing to do. But what we do know is that treatment generally has better outcomes if it is sought early; so the earlier you can face up your eating disorder and want be free of it, the better. However, recovery is possible at any stage of your life, so it is important never to give up.

They are embarrassed

Often people are embarrassed to talk to others about their binge-eating, which can prevent them from seeking professional help. It's important to remember that most medical professionals will have some understanding of eating disorders and therefore they will not be judgemental; indeed, it is likely that they will have encountered a number of people with eating disorders in the past.

They don't know what treatments are available

Many people do not get help for their eating disorder simply because they do not know what treatments are available or how to access them. This chapter will describe the most common treatment approaches and give advice on how you can get help.

Treatment settings

You can get help for your eating disorder in a number of different treatment settings. Broadly speaking there are four levels of treatment settings: self-help, out-patient, day-patient and in-patient. Self-help has been explored in the preceding chapters and the other settings will be briefly explained here. The amount of time you spend in treatment and the degree of professional input you receive varies across these settings.

Out-patient treatment

Often, people feel they need professional support to help them overcome their binge-eating problem. Usually this will happen on an out-patient basis. Out-patient treatment can be any of the psychological treatments outlined later in this chapter and may be delivered by a clinical psychologist, psychotherapist, specialist nurse or low-intensity therapy worker. Treatment may be delivered on a one-to-one basis with a therapist or within a group of people with similar eating problems.

To get professional help for your eating disorder you need to discuss your eating problem with your GP. He or she can then refer you for psychological treatment within primary care (in your GP surgery or local psychological services) or to a specialized service. Different specialist services are available depending on where you live. You may be referred to a community mental health team (CMHT), which manages people with a variety of problems and is headed by a psychiatrist; it will include nurses, psychologists, occupational therapists and psychotherapists. Alternatively, you may be referred to a specialist eating disorder service.

Wherever you are referred, you will be assessed by an out-patient team member who will ask you about your eating problems and aspects of your personal history. Discussing these issues may be difficult and could leave you feeling exposed, but it is necessary for the effective planning of your treatment.

Day- and in-patient treatment

If someone is unable to make improvements in an out-patient setting and the eating disorder is having a profound effect on that person's life, day- or in-patient treatment can be considered. Day-patient treatment programmes vary, but attendance is usually required on four or five days a week (from approximately 8 a.m. to 4 p.m.) and it is likely to include one or more communal meals. In-patient treatment involves having all your meals and sleeping in an eating disorders unit. Both treatments usually comprise therapy (individual, group and family) as well as practical advice on diet, shopping and food preparation.

Treatment approaches

This section provides a description of therapeutic approaches for treating binge-eating. This is not an exhaustive list and there are a number of other therapies available; however, these are the most commonly delivered treatments. These therapies can be offered on both a group and an individual basis.

Everyone is different: what works for some people may not work for others. It is important to remember that if a treatment doesn't work, you have *not* failed. The treatment was not right for you at that time in your life and there are other options available for you.

Cognitive behavioural therapy (CBT)

The self-help programme in this book has drawn heavily from CBT techniques. Research has consistently shown that CBT is effective for treating binge-eating in a majority of people and it is the recommended treatment approach in the UK. CBT with a therapist involves getting help to identifying unhealthy links between eating behaviours and beliefs about eating, shape and weight, and collaboratively challenging those beliefs through behavioural experiments and confronting thought patterns. A key element of the treatment is providing advice and support for establishing a pattern of regular eating throughout the day, which tends to displace many binges. An important aspect of CBT is that it involves doing homework tasks outside of therapy sessions.

Interpersonal therapy (IPT)

IPT emphasizes the ways in which a person's current relationships and social context cause or maintain eating disorder symptoms. The relationships we have with others can have a huge impact on our emotional well-being. Negative interpersonal interactions can lead to difficult emotions, which can in turn be manifested in eating-disordered behaviours. IPT encourages you to learn new and better ways of relating with people and dealing with negative interpersonal interactions. Research indicates that IPT can be effective for treating binge-eating; however, it may take longer than CBT to achieve results.

Psychodynamic therapy

Psychodynamic therapy aims to explore in depth the emotional issues underlying your eating disorder. This approach focuses on personal events and relationships (both past and present) to see how they have contributed to your current situation. The aim is to help you make connections between the past and the present to enable you to gain insight into your behaviour and identify where you might want to make changes.

Dialectic behavioural therapy (DBT)

DBT draws on strategies from CBT and Eastern spiritual practices. This approach involves simultaneous individual and group therapies which aim to develop specific skills to help the individual to overcome his or her eating problems. These skills are mindfulness (being aware of and accepting thoughts and actions that are happening in the present), interpersonal effectiveness (developing strategies to deal with interpersonal interactions) and distress tolerance (learning how to tolerate and survive painful emotions), and work towards enabling emotional regulation. DBT is most appropriate when a difficulty in regulating emotions is at the root of an individual's eating disorder.

Family or couple therapy

Eating disorders do not only affect the individual, but families and partners as well. Family therapy and couple therapy intend to 'treat' everyone in attendance. Such therapy aims to help show how family members can be supportive throughout the recovery process, as well as allowing them to investigate how the eating disorder has affected their own lives.

It is usually conducted in a room with a one-way mirror, enabling the session to be observed by a second party. Different perspectives allow more complicated family dynamics to be seen. Family therapy is commonly used when treating children but can be useful for individuals of all ages.

Cognitive analytic therapy

Cognitive analytic therapy is a collaborative, structured therapy which works by helping you to identify your patterns of relating to others and exploring how these may affect your current difficulties. The way in which you relate to others is thought to stem from patterns of interaction in childhood. Therapy focuses on helping you identify and recognize when these patterns occur, and find exits from unhelpful patterns. Key elements of therapy include a collaboratively constructed diagram (identifying and revising the old patterns), letters written by you and your therapist (understanding the problematic patterns and outlining change) and using the therapeutic relationship to explore your ways of relating to others.

Antidepressants

Taking antidepressant drugs can reduce the frequency of binge-eating. Selective serotonin reuptake inhibitors (SSRIs), specifically fluoxetine, are the drugs of first choice in terms of tolerability and reduction of symptoms. However, evidence suggests the treatment effects are short-lived and that there are no long-term benefits.

Appendix 1

What is an average portion?

Starchy carbohydrate foods

Bread

- 2 medium slices from a large loaf or 3 medium slices from a small loaf
- 1 medium bread roll
- 1 large or 2 small pitta bread
- 1 average bagel
- 1 large 'bread' muffin
- 2 crumpets
- 10 cm (4 in) 'thick' French stick or 15 cm (6 in) 'thin' French stick
- 4–5 crispbread (e.g. Ryvita or similar) or 4 oatcakes or 5 crackers (e.g. cream crackers).

Potato

- 4–5 egg-sized new potatoes (6–8 baby potatoes)
- 200–250 g potato (before cooking), either as jacket or to boil for mash
- 4 pieces boiled potato (same weight as potato above)
- 2 scoops or 3 heaped tablespoons mashed potato
- 150 g oven chips (frozen weight) or 2 heaped serving spoons
- 3 small or 2 medium roast potatoes (total weight approximately 150 g)
- 2 potato waffles or 3 hash browns.

Other carbohydrates

- 75g (dry weight) pasta or couscous (2 heaped serving spoons cooked weight)
- 60 g (dry weight) rice (2 heaped serving spoons cooked weight)
- 1 individual portion boil-in-the-bag rice, or according to the portion size on the packet

- 1 Yorkshire pudding equals half a portion of carbohydrate, so you would need half a portion of potato.

Fresh pasta, etc.

- plain (e.g. tagliatelle, spaghetti): 90–100 g, or preferably follow portion guide on packet
- filled (e.g. salmon, ham, cheese tortellini): 125–175 g, plus vegetables (e.g. tomato sauce with roasted vegetables). NB: If using shop-bought sauce, there is no need to add fat
- 125 g gnocchi
- 50 g noodles (one block).

Pastry

If it completely surrounds food (e.g. pie, pasty, salmon en croute), this counts as your whole carbohydrate and fat portion.

Quiche, or dishes with only a base and/or a side covering of pastry, need a further half-portion of carbohydrate and half-portion of fat.

Protein foods

Meat

Red meat (beef, lamb, pork, ham)

- 3–4 average slices (75–100 g) cooked weight (e.g. for sandwiches, roast dinner)
- 100–150 g uncooked weight (e.g. mince)
- 170 g meat on the bone (e.g. 1 large pork chop, 2 small lamb chops)
- 2 large sausages or 1 large Frankfurter
- 1 large beef burger (approx. 100 g or a quarter-pounder) or 2 small beef burgers
- 50g pâté (meat).

Poultry

- 4–5 average slices (100–125 g) cooked weight chicken or turkey (e.g. for sandwiches, roast dinner)
- meat with no bone: e.g. 1 average chicken breast (125–150g uncooked weight)

- meat on the bone: e.g. 1 average chicken leg or 2 chicken thighs or drumsticks or 3–4 chicken wings (170–200 g uncooked weight).

Fish

- white fish (cod, plaice): 150–180 g uncooked weight
- oily fish (salmon or tuna steak): 125–150 g uncooked weight
- fish on the bone (e.g. herring, mackerel): 1 average-sized fish (about 230 g in total)
- prawns: 60 g (defrosted, if frozen) plus 1 dessertspoon mayonnaise or equivalent; 120–180 g if served without sauce
- 1 x 200 g tin (drained) tuna or salmon in brine or water, or half a 200 g tin (drained) fish in oil
- 2–3 individual small fish (e.g. canned or fresh sardines, pilchards)
- 3 fish fingers or 2 standard-size fish cakes or 1 premium fish cake (chilled, not frozen).

Vegetarian

- 2 medium eggs
- 200 g baked beans
- 60 g (pre-cooked weight) lentils, beans, chickpeas, etc.
- 150 g (cooked weight) or half of 400 g tin (drained) lentils, beans, pulses
- vegetable-based pâté, e.g. chickpea and black olive: 1 packet, 115 g
- cheese-based pâté, e.g. celery, Stilton and walnut: 50–75 g
- 30 g nuts (e.g. peanuts, cashew, walnuts) or seeds (e.g. sesame, pumpkin)
- 30 g or 2 heaped teaspoons peanut butter
- 2 heaped tablespoons or half a 170 g pot hummus
- 150 g plain Quorn or tofu or 75 g marinated tofu (half a 150g pack)
- 1 large or 2 small Quorn fillets
- 2 small or 1 large vegeburger, bean burger or nut cutlet
- half-pack of Beanfeast
- 2 large or 3 smaller vegetarian sausages.

Vegetables, salads and fruit

Vegetables

The following are equivalent to one portion of vegetables, which is the right amount for a main meal. You can chose to have one item from the list or a combination, but if you do eat a combination be careful not to eat an excessive amount (see below):

- 3 heaped tablespoons vegetables (e.g. peas, sweetcorn, cabbage, swede, mushrooms)
- half a large courgette or pepper
- 2 spears broccoli or 8 small florets cauliflower
- approximately 8 Brussels sprouts
- 1 leek (white part) or 1 medium onion
- one-third of an aubergine
- half a medium avocado.

Salad

The following are equivalent to one portion of salad. As with vegetables, you can choose to eat just one item from the list or a selection, but again, it is important to watch the portion size.

- 1 medium tomato or 7 cherry tomatoes
- a 5-cm (2-inch) piece of cucumber
- 1 cereal bowl of mixed salad (e.g. tomatoes, cucumber and lettuce)
- 3 sticks celery.

It is important to ensure that you avoid giving yourself too large a portion of vegetables or salad with a meal. This is because it will make the meal quite bulky and more filling, meaning that you may struggle to eat the whole meal. This is especially true if you are a low weight and in the initial phase of treatment. However, this will improve as your eating pattern improves and weight increases. If you feel it is difficult to limit vegetables and salad try the following guidelines:

- Serve the vegetables or salad *after* you have served yourself the other foods.

- Use a small individual side plate or bowl for salads.

Fruit (eaten with light dessert, breakfast or as a light snack)

The following is a guide to what constitutes a portion of fruit:

- 1 apple, medium banana, orange, nectarine or peach
- half a grapefruit
- 2 medium-sized fruits (e.g. plums, kiwi fruit, clementines, tangerines or satsumas)
- 3 small fruits or dried fruits (e.g. apricots, dates, prunes)
- other dried fruit (e.g. currants, sultanas): 1 tablespoon (NB: if having as an equivalent snack to biscuits, the portion size is bigger; see snack list on pages 110–11 for details)
- large fruits: a 5-cm (2-inch) slice of melon, 2 x 5-cm slices of mango, 1 large slice fresh pineapple
- 200 ml orange or other fruit juice or smoothie (only counts once per day)
- handful of grapes (approx. 15).

Dairy

- 45–50 g hard cheese (Cheddar, Edam, halloumi)
- 125–150 g pot of cottage cheese
- 45–50 g creamy cheese (cream cheese, Brie, feta, goat's cheese)
- milk-based sauce (e.g. cheese or white sauce): 1 teacupful or serving size on packet.

Fats

- 2 teaspoons (1 dessertspoon) butter or margarine
- 2 teaspoons (1 dessertspoon) oil
- 2 teaspoons (1 dessertspoon) or 1 sachet mayonnaise
- 1 heaped tablespoon (4 teaspoons) or 2 sachets salad cream
- 3 teaspoons (1 tablespoon) oil-based dressing
- 1 rounded tablespoon pesto.

Snack list

Daily snacks

Examples of appropriate snacks to be included into your regular meal plan. Eat two or three per day as part of your healthy eating plan.

- 2 digestive biscuits (or HobNobs, shortcake)
- 3 fruit shortcake biscuits (or ginger nuts, rich tea, garibaldi or similar, e.g. small snack pack)
- 3 Jaffa Cakes (available in snack packs)
- 1 packet crisps or savoury snacks (25–40 g)
- 4–6 dates, figs or prunes; or 60 g currants or raisins; or 40g dried fruit and nut mix
- 30 g nuts and seeds (e.g. peanuts, cashew nuts, pumpkin seeds)
- 1 cereal bar (e.g. Jordan's, Nutrigrain, Tracker, Fruesli) – usually 25–35 g
- flapjack – approx. 30–35 g
- 1 slice toast with 1 teaspoon margarine or butter and jam, Marmite or peanut butter
- small chocolate bar or biscuit (e.g. Flake, Creme Egg, Club biscuit) – around 35 g
- small scone, rock cake or fruit bun (no icing) – around 40 g
- 200 ml milk or flavoured milk
- 1 pot yoghurt (not diet)
- 1 piece of fruit
- 2 crackers or 2 Ryvita or 3 crispbread crackers, plus 1 slice cheese (20 g) or 1 tablespoon peanut butter or pesto or 2 tablespoons hummus or avocado
- 1 scoop ice cream
- 1 medium slice fruit toast with 1 teaspoon butter or margarine
- 1 small chocolate bar.

More substantial snacks or desserts

Aim to have two or three of these per week as part of your plan.

- 1 slice carrot cake, gateau or similar, or 1 average slice of cake
- 1 Danish pastry, doughnut, Belgian bun, iced bun or similar
- 1 pain au raisin, pain au chocolate or almond croissant

- 1 American-style muffin (standard size, around 75–100 g)
- 1 individual slice cheesecake (around 75–100 g)
- 1 standard chocolate bar (around 50 g), e.g. Mars, a two-finger Twix, Snickers)
- 1 average portion of crumble, sponge or fruit pie with custard (150 ml or 1 average ladleful), 1 scoop ice cream or 2 tablespoons double cream
- 1 individual bar of flapjack, around 70–100 g
- 1 luxury ice cream bar, e.g. Magnum, Haagen-Dazs Dulce de Leche
- 125 g/ml or 3 scoops luxury ice cream, e.g. Haagen-Dazs, Ben and Jerry's, Thornton's
- 50–60 g bag crisps or savoury snacks, e.g. McCoy's, Kettle, Walker's Max, prawn crackers
- 1 regular McDonald's or similar takeaway thick milkshake
- 1 non-fruit Corner yogurt (e.g. Lemon Cheesecake Corner, Mississippi Mud Pie Corner) – 150 g pot
- standard Müller Rice dessert (e.g. vanilla custard or chocolate)
- 1 muesli bar and 2 cookies
- 1 carton yoghurt and 1 large banana
- 400 ml flavoured milk
- 250 ml fruit juice and 1 muesli bar and 1 serving fruit
- 2 pieces of medium sliced toast or bread with 2 teaspoons butter or margarine and 2 teaspoons jam or honey
- bowl of cereal with 200 ml semi-skimmed milk
- 50 g roasted nuts
- 30 g nuts and 250 ml juice
- 1 large muffin or large fruit scone
- smoothie made with 250 ml semi-skimmed milk and 1 large banana.

Appendix 2

Weight charts

	Height														
Metres	1.42	1.45	1.47	1.50	1.52	1.55	1.58	1.60	1.63	1.65	1.68	1.70	1.73	1.75	1.78
Feet/ inches	4′ 8″	4′ 9″	4′ 10″	4′ 11″	5′ 0″	5′ 1″	5′ 2″	5′ 3″	5′ 4″	5′ 5″	5′ 6″	5′ 7″	5′ 8″	5′ 9″	5′ 10″
Age															
15	38.1	39.9	41.7	43.5	45.4	47.2	49.0	50.8	52.2	54.0	55.8	57.6	59.4	61.2	63.0
16	40.8	42.2	44.0	45.4	47.2	48.5	50.3	51.7	53.5	54.9	56.7	58.1	59.9	61.2	63.0
17	42.6	44.0	45.8	47.2	48.5	49.9	51.3	53.1	54.4	55.8	57.2	58.5	60.3	61.7	63.0
18	43.5	44.9	46.3	47.6	49.4	50.8	52.2	53.5	54.9	56.7	58.1	59.4	60.8	62.1	64.0
19	44.0	45.4	46.7	48.1	49.9	51.3	52.6	54.0	55.3	57.2	58.5	59.9	61.2	62.6	64.4
20	44.5	45.8	47.2	48.5	49.9	51.7	53.1	54.4	55.8	57.2	59.0	60.3	61.7	63.0	64.4
21	44.5	45.8	47.2	49.0	50.3	51.7	53.1	54.4	56.2	57.6	59.0	60.3	61.7	63.5	64.9
22	44.5	46.3	47.6	49.0	50.3	51.7	53.5	54.9	56.2	57.6	59.0	60.8	62.1	63.5	64.9
23	44.5	46.3	47.6	49.0	50.3	51.7	53.5	54.9	56.2	57.6	59.0	60.8	62.1	63.5	64.9
24	44.9	46.3	48.1	49.4	50.8	52.2	53.5	54.9	56.2	57.6	59.0	60.3	61.7	63.5	64.9
27	45.4	46.7	48.1	49.4	50.8	52.6	54.0	55.3	56.7	58.1	59.4	60.8	62.1	63.5	65.3
32	46.7	48.1	49.4	50.8	52.2	53.5	54.9	56.2	57.6	59.0	60.3	61.7	63.0	64.4	65.8
37	48.1	49.4	50.8	52.2	53.5	54.9	56.2	57.6	59.0	60.3	61.7	63.0	64.4	65.8	67.1
42	50.3	51.7	53.1	54.4	55.8	57.2	58.5	59.9	60.8	62.1	63.5	64.9	66.2	67.6	68.9
47	52.2	53.5	54.4	55.8	57.2	58.5	59.9	61.2	62.6	64.0	65.3	66.2	67.6	68.9	70.3
52	53.1	54.4	55.8	57.2	58.1	59.4	60.8	62.1	63.5	64.4	65.8	67.1	68.5	69.9	70.8
57	53.1	54.4	55.8	57.2	58.5	59.4	60.8	62.1	63.5	64.9	65.8	67.1	68.5	69.9	71.2
62	52.6	54.0	55.3	56.2	57.6	59.0	60.3	61.7	62.6	64.0	65.3	66.7	68.0	68.9	70.3
67	51.3	52.6	54.0	55.3	56.2	57.6	59.0	60.3	61.7	62.6	64.0	65.3	66.7	68.0	68.9

Graduated mean weights (kgs) at each age and height: females

	Height														
Metres	1.52	1.55	1.58	1.60	1.63	1.65	1.68	1.70	1.73	1.75	1.78	1.80	1.83	1.85	1.88
Feet/ inches	5′ 0″	5′ 1″	5′ 2″	5′ 3″	5′ 4″	5′ 5″	5′ 6″	5′ 7″	5′ 8″	5′ 9″	5′ 10″	5′ 11″	6′ 0″	6′ 1″	6′ 2″
Age															
15	43.5	45.8	47.6	49.4	51.3	53.1	55.3	57.2	59.0	60.8	62.6	64.9	66.7	68.5	70.3
16	44.9	47.2	49.0	50.8	52.6	54.4	56.2	58.1	59.9	61.7	63.5	66.2	67.6	69.4	71.2
17	46.7	48.5	50.3	52.2	54.4	55.8	57.6	59.4	61.2	63.0	64.9	66.7	68.5	70.3	72.1
18	48.1	49.9	51.3	53.1	54.9	56.7	58.5	60.3	62.1	64.0	65.8	67.1	68.9	70.8	72.6
19	49.4	50.8	52.6	54.4	56.2	58.1	59.9	61.2	63.0	64.9	66.7	68.0	69.9	71.7	73.5
20	50.3	52.2	54.0	55.3	57.2	59.0	60.8	62.1	64.0	65.8	67.1	68.9	70.8	72.1	73.9
21	51.7	53.1	54.9	56.2	58.1	59.9	61.2	63.0	64.4	66.2	68.0	69.4	71.2	72.6	74.4
22	52.2	54.0	55.3	57.2	59.0	60.3	62.1	63.5	65.3	67.1	68.5	70.3	71.7	73.5	75.3
23	52.6	54.4	56.2	57.6	59.4	60.8	62.6	64.4	65.8	67.6	68.9	70.8	72.6	73.9	75.8
24	53.1	54.9	56.2	58.1	59.9	61.2	63.0	64.4	66.2	68.0	69.4	71.2	72.6	74.4	76.2
27	53.5	54.9	56.7	58.5	59.9	61.7	63.5	65.3	66.7	68.5	70.3	71.7	73.5	75.3	76.7
32	54.4	55.8	57.6	59.4	60.8	62.6	64.4	66.2	67.6	69.4	71.2	72.6	74.4	76.2	78.0
37	54.9	56.2	58.1	59.9	61.7	63.0	64.9	66.7	68.0	69.9	71.7	73.5	74.8	76.7	78.5
42	54.9	56.7	58.1	59.9	61.7	63.0	64.9	66.7	68.0	69.9	71.7	73.5	74.8	76.7	78.5
47	55.3	56.7	58.5	60.3	61.7	63.5	65.3	67.1	68.5	70.3	72.1	73.5	75.3	77.1	78.9
52	55.3	57.2	59.0	60.8	62.1	64.0	65.8	67.1	68.9	70.8	72.1	73.9	75.8	77.1	78.9
57	55.8	57.6	59.4	60.8	62.6	64.4	66.2	67.6	69.4	71.2	72.6	74.4	76.2	77.6	79.4
62	56.2	58.1	59.9	61.2	63.0	64.9	66.2	68.0	69.9	71.7	73.0	74.8	76.7	78.0	79.8
67	56.7	58.5	60.3	61.7	63.5	65.3	66.7	68.5	70.3	71.7	73.5	75.3	77.1	78.5	80.3

Graduated mean weights (kgs) at each age and height: males

Appendix 3
Recovery stories

F's recovery story

All my memories of childhood are happy ones. I grew up in a nice neighbourhood, with a loving mum (I never knew my dad) and lots of friends. At primary school I was a high achiever and usually all my work was top of the class. I was popular with girls and boys. At age 11 I won a scholarship to attend private school and, feeling I should take this opportunity to make my mum proud, I opted to leave all my friends and attend this new school.

All my memories of secondary school are unhappy ones. From the day I started my new school, I knew I was different. I was no longer top of the class, I no longer stood out from the rest of the people in my class and I had very few friends. I drifted apart from my old friends now that they were all at different schools, and I just didn't seem to be able to make new friends. I always felt I just didn't fit in. I felt excluded, I felt lonely and I felt completely worthless. As soon as the school bell finished I would run home and hide in my room, desperately doing school work to try and compete with my classmates. My mum now thought I was old enough to have my own key, so I could go home by myself while she could focus on her career. Some nights she didn't come home until I was asleep. It was at this time that I found relief in food. Mum was working longer hours and had little time to talk to me, but instead bought me chocolate as a peace offering. The chocolate tasted good and the time eating it just seemed to rid me of all the negative emotions I was feeling. I gradually started to eat more and more chocolate and whatever else I could find in the cupboards. Initially this was crisps and sweets, but it moved on to be whole loaves of bread and butter which I would pick up from the shop on my way home. Being home alone most nights, I would never have a regular meal, although I always told Mum I had had one.

Looking back, food was my only friend. Bingeing became the only thing that I got pleasure out of, and the only thing I had control of. It was only when the name-calling started that I realized how much weight I had put on through the bingeing. The comments were hurtful: 'fatty', 'thunder thighs' – I got them all. At school I would skip lunch so people wouldn't see me eating. By home time I was starving and this made me hide deeper in my bingeing, only this time I thought if I made myself sick I wouldn't put on the weight and the name-calling would stop.

I guess I was now officially bulimic. It happened so quickly and without me even being aware, but I was stuck with it and it wouldn't go away. I was even more alone and, having nobody to confide in, bulimia became my only friend for nine months. I guess deep down I was craving for some kind of attention. It was eventually a relief when my mum caught me being sick one weekend and straight away referred me to a therapist. I felt ashamed, embarrassed and fearful of what people, including my therapist, might think of me.

I started a course of CBT which challenged all my feelings of worthlessness. I was not useless and I was not stupid – in fact, through just looking at my school results in comparison to the national average I was way above what was expected for someone my age. I just hadn't been able to see it before now, being sheltered in the high-pressure environment of my school. I was taught new ways to cope with my emotions, and I was taught how to be open and honest about my feelings. I realized that, being an only child and having no father figure, I needed my mum more than I thought, and we were able to address this. My mum was able to cut her working hours to make more time for me. Diet plans helped me get my eating back on track; it was so surprising how regular evening meals made me less hungry and therefore my bingeing reduced.

Through placing my trust in the therapist I was able to take on board what she was saying. At first I thought, 'No way am I doing that!' but she gently encouraged me to try things. We did different experiments each week. For example, one week my challenge was to go swimming. I was terrified that people would stare at me, but I did it and nothing bad happened, and I realized people weren't all looking at me and going to shout hurtful comments. Another time I found that a kick-boxing session at the gym was a better source of relieving stress for me than going straight home after school.

Therapy made me realize how unhappy my new school had made me. My mum agreed I could leave my private school and attend the local comprehensive where all my friends were. It didn't all work out at first, as everyone had made new friends, but with time I started to develop friendships once again.

My journey through bulimia was not an easy one. I was one of the lucky ones in that it was recognized and I was able to conquer it. Therapy for me was the best cure, but it took a very personal therapist to build my trust to try new things. Making simple changes to my life completely altered my way of thinking, and this has made me a much happier person. The best thing I have discovered since leaving my bulimia behind is that I can have fun and I can make friends. Being open and honest with people means you don't have to lock everything up inside and you don't have to battle on alone.

C's recovery from bulimia nervosa

I cannot remember exactly when I first developed my eating disorder. Looking back now it was a massive part of most of my life, but I suppose it all started to a certain extent during my first year of college when I was 17. Moving from secondary school was a huge step for me, especially as I was going to a different college from the majority of my close friends. Would anyone like me? Was I going to make friends? Was I going to reach my potential? I had so many worries flying round my head.

Initially it started okay; I liked my classes and teachers and most of the other kids were nice, although I always felt 'different' and didn't fit in with any of the cliques already made: not pretty enough, sporty enough, clever enough . . . PE was what I disliked the most – I hated getting changed in front of all the other girls, I couldn't understand why it was compulsory to do it once a week and I hated it. They were all so much thinner and prettier than me, and all of the boys were interested in them. I was always picked last as I wasn't the most sporty person, much to the delight of the pretty, popular girls. I felt so inadequate and jealous of them and their confidence. Walking home I used to feel taunted by their snide remarks and sniggering during these classes, their comments from the changing rooms echoing in my head. I had nobody to talk to about how tough I was finding everything: my mum was too busy, and my sister had managed so why couldn't I? I didn't want to be a letdown.

I would save money from my part-time job and spend it on food on the way home – sweets, chocolate, crisps, anything and everything I could buy with what money I had – eating all of it at once before I got home. I felt disgusted and embarrassed with myself about what I was doing, but could not stop. It became a major part of my day – planning what I was going to buy on my way home from school that day. But the guilt I would feel afterwards was unbearable so I would vomit, which later developed into laxative use. I think I did pretty well in hiding all of this from my family and people at college.

This vicious cycle of binge–purge behaviour continued for about 18 months, getting gradually worse and a larger part of my life, not to mention the feelings of self-disgust and shame about my body and what I was doing.

I have always had great ambitions academically: I wanted to have a career within healthcare, and wanted to go to university. My A levels were looming and I realized that I needed to do something about my eating if I wanted to go to university and fulfil all of my dreams. I decided to talk to my mum about everything, instantly feeling so much relief in sharing my problems, and realizing she was on my side and was going to help me get through this. I saw my GP and was referred to a local psychology service; although it took a long wait to get CBT with a psychologist, I got dietetic help and was recommended several self-help books, and my mum was a huge help. I think I felt that because I didn't look as though I had an eating disorder people would not take me seriously – but this was not the case.

Today I am still coming to terms with my body and being myself, having CBT weekly. Recovery has not been easy and has not been instantaneous, but with support and determination I am getting there – and other people can do the same. I intend to go to university next year, and to leave my bulimia at home.

Useful addresses

UK and Ireland

Anorexia & Bulimia Care (ABC)
Providence House
The Borough
Wedmore
Somerset BS28 4EG
Tel.: 01934 713789
Sufferer's Helpline: 01934 710679
Parent Helpline: 01934 710645
Website: www.anorexiabulimiacare.co.uk

A Christian organization for people with eating disorders and their carers.

beat (the working name of the **Eating Disorders Association)**
103 Prince of Wales Road
Norwich NR1 1DW
Tel.: 01603 619090
Helpline: 0845 634 1414 (10.30 a.m. to 8.30 p.m., Monday to Friday; 1 p.m. to 4.30 p.m., Saturdays)
Youthline: 0845 634 7650 (4.30 p.m. to 8.30 p.m., Monday to Friday; 1 p.m. to 4.30 p.m., Saturdays)
Website: www.b-eat.co.uk

The essential first point of contact for people with bulimia, this is a UK-based charitable organization that offers information, help and assistance to clients, carers and professionals.

Bodywhys – The Eating Disorder Association of Ireland
PO Box 105
Blackrock
Co. Dublin
Tel.: 01 283 4963
Helpline: 1890 200 444
Website: www.bodywhys.ie

An Irish national charity that provides information and support to people with eating disorders and their families.

Mental Health Foundation (London office)
Ninth floor, Sea Containers House
20 Upper Ground
London SE1 9QB
Tel.: 020 7803 1100 (to find out about their work)
Website: www.mentalhealth.org.uk

A UK charity providing information on mental health issues, including eating disorders.

Mental Health Foundation (Scotland office)
Merchants House
30 George Square
Glasgow G2 1EG
Tel.: 0141 572 0125

Mental Health Foundation (Wales office)
Merlin House
No. 1 Langstone Business Park
Priory Drive
Newport NP18 2HJ
Tel.: 01633 415434

St George's National Eating Disorders Service
Building 28, Trust Headquarters
South West London and St George's Mental Health NHS Trust
Springfield University Hospital
61 Glenburnie Road
London SW17 7DJ
Tel.: 020 8682 6000
Website: www.swlstg-tr.nhs.uk/specialities/eating_disorders.asp

Provides assessment, care and treatment for adults aged 18 and over with eating disorders who are referred through community mental health teams locally and nationwide

Samaritans
Chris
PO Box 9090
Stirling FK8 2SA
Tel.: 08457 909090 (free, 24 hours a day)
Website: www.samaritans.org

Offers confidential, non-judgemental emotional support to people who are experiencing feelings of distress or despair.

USA

National Eating Disorders Association
603 Stewart Street, Suite 803
Seattle
WA 98101
Tel.: 206 382 3587 (8 a.m. to 5 p.m., Pacific time)
Toll-free Information and Referral Helpline: 1 800 931 2237 (8.30 a.m. to 4.30 p.m., Pacific time)
Website: www.nationaleatingdisorders.org

Websites

BBC Health
www.bbc.co.uk/health

The mental health section contains information on eating disorders.

Counselling
www.counselling.ltd.uk

A charity which puts people in touch with counsellors and psychotherapists in their area, some of whom offer free or low-cost services.

Mental Health Care
www.mentalhealthcare.org.uk

A resource website run by the Institute of Psychiatry at King's College London.

Mirror Mirror
www.mirror-mirror.org

A US website that provides, on a self-help basis, information on eating disorders, getting help, recovery, and so on, as well as links to other websites.

Further reading

Cooper, Myra, Todd, Gillian and Wells, Adrian, *Bulimia Nervosa: A cognitive therapy programme for clients*. Jessica Kingsley, London, 2000.

Treasure, Janet and Schmidt, Ulrike, *Getting Better Bit(e) by Bit(e): A survival kit for sufferers of bulimia nervosa and binge eating disorders*. Routledge, London, 1997.

Treasure, Janet, Smith, Gráinne and Crane, Anna, *Skills-based Learning for Caring for a Loved One with an Eating Disorder: The new Maudsley method*. Routledge, London, 2007.

Waller, Glenn *et al.*, *Cognitive Behavioral Therapy for Eating Disorders: A comprehensive treatment guide*. Cambridge University Press, New York, 2007.

Index